NEVER FOR SALE

Little Free Library

Ken Courtade, Realtor

ALWAYS FOR FREE

GREEN YOUR HOME

Healthy, Money-Smart, and Sustainable Living Begins at Home

A KELLER WILLIAMS® REALTY GUIDE

Produced by KellerInk

1234567890 DOC/DOC 0987

ISBN 978-1-932649-19-2

This publication is designed to provide accurate and authoritative information in regard to the subject matter covered. It is sold with the understanding that neither the author nor the publisher is engaged in rendering legal, accounting, or other professional service. If legal advice or other expert assistance is required, the services of a competent professional person should be sought.

— From a Declaration of Principles jointly adopted by a Committee
of the American Bar Association and a Committee of Publishers

Citibank, N.A., equal housing lender and Member FDIC. Citi, Citibank, Arc Design and Citi with Arc Design are registered service marks of Citigroup Inc.

OUR MISSION

At Keller Williams Realty, we care about the place you call home. We understand that it's more than a collection of concrete, wood, and steel. It's more than an asset to be bought and sold. It's where you feel safe, where you can take a deep breath, where you gather with your family and friends, and where you build your strength.

Since our founding, it has been our company's stated mission to build careers worth having, businesses worth owning, and lives worth living. We realize now, more than ever, that a life worth living is one that is healthy, money smart, and sustainable—priorities that are essential to the "Green Your Home" model. Greening your home not only builds lasting value in what is yours, but it cements a life worth living for future generations.

OUR BELIEF

We believe that greening your home is a quality-of-life choice for here and now, as well as a necessary step to protect our planet and its resources for future generations. We trust in the power of individuals and their ability to learn, change, and make sustainable choices. We believe that now is the time to start—and that change begins at home.

CONTENTS

FOREWORD

Today's population uses in one day what it took the world
10,000 days to create.

PAUL HAWKEN, *THE ECOLOGY OF COMMERCE*

WHY ISN'T EVERYONE ALREADY GREEN?

We can't watch TV, go shopping, or dine at a restaurant without "seeing green"—*locally grown, organic, biodegradable, sustainable.* We now know that most every decision we make these days has an environmental consequence and a green alternative—*recycled, energy efficient, chemical free, eco-friendly.*

What troubles me is that all of this exposure may be clouding our view and creating a sort of "green fatigue" in the world—a collective desensitization that's beginning to feel more like a fad or a fashion statement instead of an urgent call to arms. It's starting to feel a little squishy instead of dire. If we want to get to a place where everyone is thinking and living green, then, in truth, we have a long way to go.

SO WHY AREN'T WE "SEEING GREEN" IN EVERYTHING WE DO?

I think the answer comes down to three fundamental reasons: our mindset, our habits, and our lifestyle. In other words: what we think, how we behave, and how we're accustomed to living. Because they each require change, together these three challenges prevent us from easily going green. It is difficult to swim against the current, so we continue to live in a way that is out of balance with our available resources. It's simply unsustainable.

We know that we have our work cut out for us. I'm confident that together we can green our mindsets, change our habits, and adjust our lifestyles for the better. Not just for the here and now, but for the future too. When I look at my professional world—the housing and building industry—I can see that this may be the best place to begin. Since the housing and building industry accounts for nearly 40 percent of the world's energy and raw material consumption,[*] our ability to green our home lives truly has the ability to change the world. Will you join us on this journey?

Onward!
Gary Keller
Cofounder and Chairman of the Board
Keller Williams Realty, Inc.

---

[*]   Johnston, David, and Master, Kim."Green Remodeling: Changing the World One Room at a Time." Canada: New Society Publishers, 2004

ACKNOWLEDGMENTS

As you embark on your Green Your Home journey, you'll soon discover that it's an adventure you rarely take alone. From green consultants to skilled tradespeople, there are a host of experts out there who can help you each step along the way. It's an adventure not unlike the one we took as we set out to write this book. We'd now like to thank the many people who contributed their time and expertise during this book's creation.

First and foremost, thanks to the homeowners who shared stories of their green renovations and lessons learned: Sara Alvarado, Marilyn Barber, Daniela Bell, Ed and Ellen Bond, Dale and Pat Bulla, Greg and Susan Corman, Eric Foster, Steve and Beth Griffith, Diana Guidry, Jason and Jennifer La Fleur, Pat Lando, Michael McFadden, Jeff Miner, Martin and Melissa Scanlan, Jason and Lisa Spangler, Ron and Shelly Suzuki, Anna Weier, and Wanda Zinski.

Also, thank you to the industry experts who shared their specialized expertise and guidance, including green real estate professionals Matt Fetick, Gayle Fleming, Michelle Foy, Ben Kaufman, Cheryl King, Cynthia Lippert, Julie Nelson, Jennifer Rupnow, Craig Schriber, Doug Sutton, Mike Tavener, and Ken Williams, as well as the following green home consultants: Dr. John Beldock, Nate Burger, Joe Cooper, Tom Liptan, Dan Morris, and John Stovall. We also want to express our gratitude to the green architects, designers, and builders we interviewed, especially Scott Blunk, Hunter Ten Broeck, Ben Falk, Dean Hill, Craig Jenkins-Sutton, Ron Mann, Rich Radford, Marcus Renner, Alan Rossing, and Ron Wickman. Finally, we want to give a special shout-out to the members of our Green Leadership Council who advocated for this book from day one: Ron Armstrong, Vida Ash, Judy Farr, Chuck Frankel, Stuart Galvis, Mary-Anne Gillespie, Janice Hall, Nan Cie Hamilton, Cheryl King, Helen Martin, and Colleen McLean.

We're grateful to the following organizations and entities for their robust data and research on green living issues: the Asthma Society of Canada, Beyond Pesticides, California Energy Commission, Circle of Blue, EcoBroker, Health Canada, National Aeronautics and Space Administration, National Association of Home Builders, National Association of Realtors and their NAR Green Designation, National Audubon Society, National Center for Environmental Health, National Fenestration Rating Council, National Gardening Association, National Pesticide Information Center, Natural Resources Canada, U.S. Department of Energy, U.S. Energy Information Administration, and the U.S. Environmental Protection Agency.

Conceiving, researching, writing, and producing this book was a three-year journey, and many talented individuals played key roles. Writer Rachel Proctor May took our original outline, researched it extensively through books and interviews, and produced an excellent early draft. Her fingerprints are throughout. She worked closely with our editors—first Mark McFarlane and later, Jonas Koffler. Jonas, in particular, dedicated many months to this project and helped execute a number of important revisions. Without Jonas' dedication, this book might never have happened. Artist Dave Bregande contributed some terrific art, which you'll find in our case studies. Lastly, we called on writer and editor Katie Ford to lend her fresh perspective to the work and to perform a final round of editing and revision which resulted in the book you now hold in your hands.

Our crack team at Keller Williams Realty International also deserves a big shout-out: Victoria Schneider Lukachik for ferreting out numbers, facts, and quotes through her research, as well as timely editing support; Tamara Hurwitz for leading the production team of Jeff Ryder, Maryanne Jordan, Jennifer Boyd, and Mary Keith Trawick; Teresa Metcalf for expertly coordinating all tasks and communications; Ellen Marks for her marketing eye, writing contributions, and wisdom to recommend Katie for the job, as well as her creative cohorts Annie Switt, Michael Balistreri, Hiliary Kolb, Caitlin McIntosh, Amber Presley, Laura Price, and Dustin Struhall; Anthony Azar, Tom Freireich, and Danny Thompson for championing this book to our agent, broker, and vendor partners. Mary Tennant, Mark Willis, Mo Anderson, Bryon Ellington, and Jim Talbot for lending their leadership and ideas. Finally, a huge thanks to Gary Keller who envisioned this project for what it could mean for our families, friends, professional partners and, frankly, the world.

Jay Papasan
Vice President of Publishing and Executive Editor
Austin, Texas
July 25, 2011

INTRODUCTION

American journalist Elizabeth Kolbert once wrote in an article for *National Geographic* that man's impact on Earth "may look as sudden and profound as that of an asteroid" to future geologists.

Seems a bit sensationalist, doesn't it?

That's what we thought too—until we began our research for this book. Our research team made countless inquiries into how our daily choices impact the environment and what we can do in our homes to better conserve natural resources. It turns out that Kolbert's words merely echo what scientists[*] worldwide are declaring: Human consumption in the past two centuries has released enough carbon dioxide to cause measurable, irreversible changes in the atmosphere. If we continue at this rate, we could see *in this century* climate change that would cause entire species of plants and animals to die off and our oceans to acidify to levels not recorded since an asteroid struck our planet 65 million years ago, marking the demise of the dinosaurs and the end of the Cretaceous Period.

Can you imagine that this might be our legacy? Certainly it's not what any of us want. But all signs suggest that we are marching full steam ahead in that direction. When people debate whether or not human activity is contributing

---

[*] Solomon, S., D. Qin, M. Manning, Z. Chen, M. Marquis, K.B. Averyt, M. Tignor, and H.L. Miller (eds.) "Contribution of Working Group I to the Fourth Assessment Report of the Intergovernmental Panel on Climate Change." Cambridge University Press, 2007.

to the problem, it makes us scratch our heads. If we were at sea in a boat that was taking on water, we wouldn't be arguing about whether it was a mechanical defect or human error. We would just grab a bucket and start bailing water! Instead of debating the cause of the problem, it seems wiser to be part of the solution. After all, this is the only boat we get. If it sinks, we're all sunk.

While the rise of global industrialization has magnified our impact on the environment dramatically, it also has brought about scientific discoveries and governmental policies that have catalyzed green thinking and measurable conservation efforts. In the marketplace, green-friendly products, practices, services, and materials are becoming more mainstream. However, it will be the decisions that we make in our daily lives that will have the greatest impact on what life on Earth will be like for the next generation. Indeed, it is at the grassroots level where we can make the *greenest* impact.

That's what this book is about.

GOING GREEN BEGINS AT HOME

When it comes to our environment, no matter how much we know or think we're doing to conserve and preserve, there's always room for new understanding and smarter choices. A logical place to begin your green journey is at home, the place where most of us spend the majority of our time.

Across North America, homeowners are putting increased awareness about green practices to good use. Jason and Jennifer La Fleur epitomize this trend.

A young couple, they purchased a vintage house in a wonderful neighborhood in Chicago, Illinois. From the beginning, they shared a vision of turning their old home into something even more special: a greener home. With a faith in their abilities and the helpful support of friends and family, they slowly and methodically began a step-by-step process of green retrofitting.

The limitations of their budget worked to their advantage, since Jason and Jennifer preferred doing most of the work themselves. They devoured green remodeling books, one after the next, and let careful research and smart advice from other remodelers guide them. In every aspect of the home, from the inside and internal systems to the outside, they sought opportunities—like putting in reclaimed interior doors that scream, "I'm old and beautiful!" or installing a tankless water heater. As avid gardeners, they especially loved assembling their rainwater collection system.

The La Fleurs recognized that each change they made added lasting value to the home they loved, so it was a worthwhile pursuit and a source of great pride. Each phase of their renovation felt right for them, and demonstrated to their friends and neighbors how even the smallest changes have a positive impact on the environment and on one's budget. People like Jason and Jennifer prove that a green home is attainable for anyone, even those who don't have a limitless supply of money to spend.

Echoing the money-smart approach used by the La Fleurs is the Griffith family, who live in Northern California. This party of five consists of Steve and Beth, their two kids, and Beth's mother.

Steve and Beth sought out a local company to expertly assess every inch of their home for potential green improvements— especially upgrades that would help conserve money and energy. It turns out that no matter how much they thought they were already doing to live green (such as using compact fluorescent lightbulbs and monitoring energy consumption), there was a great opportunity to do a whole lot more. The team of experts provided a road map of change to make the Griffith home healthier, more comfortable, and more efficient. Some recommended changes were no-brainers—like when their team made a startling discovery: asbestos, a dangerous carcinogen, lined the ductwork and heating system. So, before making any other changes, Steve and Beth made sure their indoor environment was safe for the family. A healthy home now became their top priority.

To address the asbestos and stay within their budget, other improvements had to be moved to their wish list. Features like a new Energy Star washing machine and roof-mounted solar panels would have to come later. Because the Griffiths planned to stay in their home for many years, they knew they'd have the opportunity to fulfill their wishes for a truly green home in time.

For many, making upgrades means making greener choices—choices that are healthier, money smart, and sustainable. There are countless ways to make your home better, from the way you furnish, clean, and maintain it to improving the way you use energy and water. In the end, remember that the home where you live, love, and create lasting memories is part of the great planetary balancing act we call "green."

CHAPTER 1:
LAYING THE GROUNDWORK

Do your little bit of good where you are; it's those little bits of good put together that overwhelm the world.

ARCHBISHOP DESMOND TUTU

A GREEN ADVENTURE AWAITS

Imagine you're preparing for a special trip. Call it the adventure of a lifetime: a safari in Africa, a trek in the Himalayas, a weeklong rafting excursion through Grand Canyon National Park with your friends and family. Maybe you'd prefer a visit to historic sites in an old-world city like Rome, Italy. Or perhaps your ideal adventure is just a relaxing week spent on a beach someplace.

No matter your preference, you would likely make your choice based on some personal priorities—the things that are most important to you. Priorities might include ensuring that your adventure enhances your sense of well-being, that you have the financial means to enjoy yourself while you're on your trip and that you have experiences rich enough to create lasting memories—stories that you can share with others.

We'd like you to think of greening your home as a similar type of adventure. Like travel, you get to shape your own experience. Greening involves planning and is often a multistep process—it takes time. Rome wasn't built in a day and you don't green a home overnight. Your green home improvement journey will be full of options. Some are more important than others, and some are more demanding. Not everyone wants to green every aspect of a home, just as not everyone wants to encounter lions in the wild while on vacation. Some prefer ease and comfort and will work with a team, some might favor a challenge and are willing to get their hands a little dirty, and others might go all out with a *I'm game for whatever it takes* mentality. You get to decide what's best for you.

FEARS AND FACTS ABOUT GOING GREEN

So, what does "green" mean to you? Does the thought of a greener home and a greener lifestyle make you excited, apprehensive, or maybe a little of both? Let's start by taking a look at some of the common fears and facts about what it means to go green. Like us, you may be surprised.

Five Fears about Going Green

1. Green is just a bunch of hype.
2. Green is too expensive a lifestyle change.
3. Green is too difficult a lifestyle change.
4. Green will not benefit me personally.
5. Green will not really make a difference.

Fear #1: Green is just a bunch of hype.

Fact #1: True "green" is anything but hype.

Sure, there are plenty of confusing messages out there. There are those who bash green and spread mistruths and those whose washed-out claims of being green are anything but the truth. So let's quickly cut through the misinformation about what green is and what it's not. At its heart, green is real, green is common sense, and green is likely already a part of your life, whether you know it or not. Your decision to go green is about a commitment to having better choices, now and in the future. Greener choices can help you save money and enable you to lead a healthier life, while conserving energy and natural resources. Is there something wrong with the idea of living more in tune with the natural world? Not at all. In fact, it's the best possible way to live.

Fear #2: Green is too expensive a lifestyle change.

Fact #2: Green can save you money over time.

Some view green homes and green lifestyles as the exclusive domain of the wealthy. Actually, this is the realm of the financially smart and the healthy. Why? Because most of the simple green actions you can take cost nothing, whether you do them at home or in your day-to-day behaviors. Think of reducing, reusing, and recycling—the basic language of going green. Instead of shrinking your bank account, going green can actually help you save money.

And if you choose not to spend a dime on new materials like solar panels or new windows, it will only cost you a little thought and effort to reuse materials and reduce your energy and water consumption habits.

For example, take a shorter daily shower and keep your thermostat set a few degrees higher in the summer and lower in the winter. Small changes like these can actually save you hundreds of dollars each year. Try them out and then compare your energy bills after a year. Should you choose to spend money on home-efficiency systems upgrades, then there's often a local, state, provincial, or federal tax incentive or rebate program available from your utility provider. In some locales, you can even take advantage of dual rebates. These add up to immediate savings and meaningful money over the long haul as energy prices rise. Being money smart is also about being healthy. Think about it: If the changes you make to your home make it less toxic, logic tells us that over time, you'll be making fewer sick visits to the doctor. That's saving more than just money.

Fear #3: Green is too difficult a lifestyle change.

Fact #3: Green is about ease and simplicity.

Green is not a complex undertaking. Green begins in our minds, and it requires us to slow down and focus our awareness a bit differently. It starts with our habits and extends throughout our homes. For many, leading a greener life might be a matter of recycling more regularly, using less water and energy at home, walking more and driving less. Are these dramatic, impossible lifestyle changes? Not at all. Keep in mind that green as a process is only as difficult as you decide to make it. You don't have to give up your car, your clothes, or your lattes and go live in the forest to be green. You can do it in more practical ways. There are different shades of green, from those who are a deeply committed dark green to the more moderately minded light green. You define your level of commitment and your vision. This book will help you identify the few green changes that can help you achieve whatever shade of green you aspire to become.

Fear #4: Green will not benefit me personally.

Fact #4: Green benefits you directly (and your neighbors too).

First and foremost, going green will make you feel good as you contribute to the well-being of the whole world. That's not just perception, that's reality. Do good, do right, and live well; enjoy the positive effect you have on others. If you're still not convinced, then let's consider what you stand to gain personally. If you can save money by consuming fewer resources and using less energy and water, is that not a material gain? If you can improve the air quality that you, your family, and your guests breathe inside your home, is that not a health gain? If you're acting as a steward of the planet for yourself and your family, imagine the millions of people in the future applauding you for your forward-thinking approach. And beyond the stewardship argument, going green is an educational and inspirational experience. Green can be a creative endeavor that's rewarding and most certainly worth doing.

Fear #5: Green will not really make a difference.

Fact #5: You alone can make all the difference in the world.

What you may perceive as impossible is actually very doable. You just need to consider where and how to begin. As an individual, every contribution you make can change the world for the better. As part of a family of billions of people, your example and influence can make a huge difference. Just by reading this book, you're already taking the first step. The point is, you can do as Mohandas Gandhi did and "be the change you wish to see in the world." Just think and act wisely. You can make a difference in your life, for your children, and for theirs.

THE GREEN YOUR HOME MODEL

When we set out to write this book, it occurred to us that green is really about understanding our priorities for a life well-lived. These are often abstract priorities, like living healthily, being money smart, or acting more sustainably. But how do we make these ideas more concrete? We can best do this through applying a three-stage model (see figure 1), which will help you understand your priorities, focus on the tangible elements and take key actions in areas of your home that matter most. We call these areas our "three green home zones," and we've organized this book around taking on specific green improvement projects in each. You'll experience this exciting process in the pages to come.

It's important to note that our model is based on extensive research of what works—the tried-and-true practices of many green-minded homeowners, including our personal green experiences. We've also taken recommendations from green-building experts and green real estate professionals from throughout the industry.

Stage One: Three Green Priorities

People choose to go green for different reasons. And it helps to recognize that every green decision we make is based upon three shared priorities in our lives: improving our health, saving money and reducing our impact on the environment. So if you're asking, "How do we know these are *the* top priorities?", you should know—you told us so!

We looked at data from the National Association of Home Builders and McGraw-Hill Construction.* Sure enough, health concerns consistently top the list along with saving money on utilities and making sustainable choices to conserve resources and protect the planet.

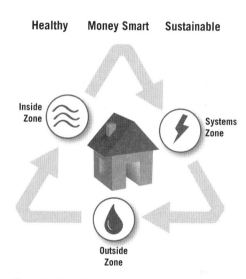

Figure 1 – Healthy, money-smart, and sustainable living are the three priorities in the Green Your Home model.

---

* "The Green Homeowner: Attitudes and Preferences for Remodeling and Buying Green Homes," SmartMarket Report. McGraw-Hill Construction, 2007.

The simplest way to address our green priorities is to ask: "Is it healthy?", "Is it money smart?", and "Is it sustainable?" Let these questions guide you when it comes to making green home improvement decisions. Are they the only considerations? No. But most homeowners agree they are what matter most.

Stage Two: Three Green Elements

In stage two, we take a look at what we've identified as the three elements of a green home: air, energy, and water. Simply put, these are the resources that we need and use every day. They're the ones that actually make life possible—and they're resources that we sometimes take for granted.

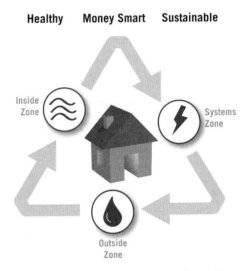

Figure 2 – The three elements of the Green Your Home model are air, energy, and water.

While our three priorities help us understand *why* we go green, the three elements that support these priorities are essential to our understanding of *what* green is about, from a very basic resource perspective. What's useful about these elements is that each one relates to our three priorities. How? The most important element of a healthy home is the air inside because it's what we breathe into our bodies and bloodstream. The most important element of a money-smart home is the energy that flows through it because we have to pay for it. And the most important element of a sustainable home is its water because it's a precious, dwindling resource. Thinking about the three elements—air, energy, and water—should help you to look at your home as a dynamic place that supports the life you live.

Stage Three: Three Green Home Zones

We're clear on our three priorities, and we understand how to think about our three supportive elements. Now comes the fun part. In stage three, we put this knowledge to use. This is the application stage, where the rubber meets the road. To be successful, we'll need to focus on the three "green home zones" listed below:

1. The Inside Zone

2. The Systems Zone

3. The Outside Zone

In each home zone, you will establish your green priorities and identify actions that will positively impact your home's air quality, energy usage, water consumption—or all three! We have done our best to map out

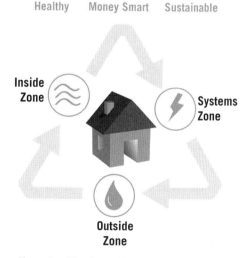

Figure 3 – The Green Your Home model includes three home zones: inside, systems, and outside.

some sure-fire Green Your Home opportunities in each home zone. Though the paths to greener living are endless in scope, this book is intended to serve as a practical guide to help you gain significant ground in becoming a green-thinking, health-conscious, money-saving machine!

1. The Inside Zone

Our inside zone refers to our home's interior living spaces, such as the rooms and nonpermanent fixtures that we can see, touch, interact with, or experience. Lighting, decorations like furniture and finishes, and flooring and appliances all fall under this zone. And so does most of our time in an average day. According to data from the U.S. Bureau of Labor and Statistics, we typically spend more than 80 percent of nonworking or commuting hours *inside* our homes. We sleep, eat, do household chores, care for others, and take on various leisure activities.

Because we spend so much of our time inside our homes, it's important we address the inside zone first and foremost. It's also important to keep in mind that while we only have twenty-four hours in a day, these days add up to a lifetime. To live long lives, our health becomes our priority. Because we spend so much of our lives inside, it only makes sense that we make a healthy inside zone our first priority. Of the three zones, the inside one is where we go to recharge and relax with our family and friends. It's our refuge.

2. The Systems Zone

The systems zone refers to the hard-working mechanical, electrical, and plumbing components that we generally can't see inside our walls, like the ducts, wiring, and pipes that make our home life easier and more comfortable, as well as the items that are bolted in place—like our central heating, ventilation, and air conditioning (HVAC) units. The systems zone is about operations and efficiency. You may compare it to the cockpit of an airplane: When you get on a plane, you know it's there, but you don't mess with it. You also rely on the captain and flight crew to know what they're doing to meet your expectations for the flight. They control the temperature levels, ventilation, and can make adjustments as needed to ensure a favorable overall experience. The same is true of the systems zone in your home, where you're in the captain's chair. When your systems zone isn't running optimally, your in-home experience isn't as good as it could be and your dollars are not being well spent. You want comfort and reliability and low maintenance at a low cost. That's being money smart, which is the top priority in the systems zone. So, it's important to look at this home zone next, as it impacts your utility bills and your pocketbook the most. And not only that, the systems zone also bridges the inside and outside zones. So it makes sense to think of it as the middle zone in the Green Your Home sequence, the zone that powers and ensures performance in your home.

3. The Outside Zone

Finally, the outside zone refers to the exterior areas of the home—features like our lawns, shade trees, flower beds, and gardens—and items attached to exterior surfaces, like gutters or awnings, or even a patio on the ground. It is the final zone when it comes to greening a home. This zone is the last one we discuss because not every homeowner has or wants an outside zone. But it's still hugely important for this Green Your Home adventure. If you have a yard or a garden or even just a balcony, it's likely you spend time there. And what you do there, like watering and planting, matters from a standpoint of sustainability.

Three priorities and three supportive elements shape your green path. Yet the bulk of your green home-improvement journey resides within each of the three home zones: your inside zone, your systems zone, and your outside zone. It's where you can select specific improvements that make sense to you and make a difference in our world—one project at a time.

Apply the 80/20 Principle when greening your home zones.

To help you put the three priorities, three elements and three zones from our model into action, here's a final point to keep in mind. You may have heard of Pareto's Principle, which is also known as the 80/20 Principle. It states that 20 percent of your efforts determine 80 percent of your results. The 20 percent is your priority. It's what you focus on most to produce a successful outcome. This concept can be applied to every aspect of our lives, from our jobs to our relationships and even our home-improvement projects.

So, what does it mean when it comes to greening our homes? It means that 20 percent of our green improvements—those practical projects we focus on most in this book—will lead to the most successful green results. We can't take on every project at the same time. Instead, we're best served by picking one project and sticking to it until it's done. It's like drawing up a list of five goals you'd like to accomplish and then picking the one that is most important. This is what you do to decide on your 20 percent.

Put another way, for the greatest results we should focus most of our efforts on the top priority in each zone (i.e., air in the inside zone or energy in the systems zone). This focus becomes the 20 percent that drives success in each of our home zones. The remainder of our efforts can be divided among the other two priorities in each zone. This is the most effective way to deliver meaningful green results.

In the inside zone of your home, the priority of being healthy is your 20 percent. It's the anchor of your everyday environment, where good air quality and abundant natural light can help ensure well-being. Focusing on projects that help you achieve this healthy outcome is what you want to do.

When given the choice, who wouldn't want the most energy-efficient, high-performance home that they can have? Comfort at a reasonable cost is the most desirable way to achieve a lower monthly utility bill. For the systems zone, the priority of being money smart is your 20 percent. Projects that deliver a cost-savings outcome are what you want to focus on in this zone.

And finally, in the outside zone, the priority of being sustainable is your 20 percent and saving water is your focus. In caring for your yard in a water-wise way, you also care for the planet and do your part to ensure water for future generations. It's a great gift and you'll never get a single word of thanks for it. But that's okay. Projects that help you while they conserve resources for the future are the best way to improve and enjoy the living landscape you call your outside zone.

Concentrating on the top priority translates to the most success in each zone. In the inside zone, it's being healthy. The systems zone is all about being money smart. And the outside zone is mostly a matter of sustainable practices.

SIX THINGS TO CONSIDER BEFORE YOU BEGIN

The first step in the Green Your Home adventure is to examine the bigger picture to determine the "big why" behind all your green improvements. There are six things to think about before you embark, and they will influence your decision making on the finer details.

Six Things to Consider Before You Begin

1. Focus on resale value.
2. Keep your climate in mind.
3. Get more for less.
4. Embrace the payback principle.
5. Take advantage of potential rebates and incentives.
6. Weigh now vs. later.

1. Focus on resale value

When Michael McFadden and his pregnant wife were planning to remodel the 1970s ranch house they bought in Kirkland, Washington, they knew they would want nontoxic finishes and sustainable features. They sealed the leaks, insulated the floor, and upgraded the appliances to efficient models. They created a nontoxic, cozy environment for their new baby. However, they also recognized that the house would probably not be their home by the time their son had his driver's license. So they also emphasized upgrades that would draw buyers when the time came to sell the home in the future.

Installing low-flow plumbing fixtures like aerated sink faucets, efficient showerheads, and dual-flush toilets is a smart, cost-effective way to green your bathroom.

"Statistically, it's the kitchen and bathroom where you get the most out of what you put into your remodel, the most return on your value," Michael says. The McFaddens developed a plan to open the awkward, cramped kitchen into a flowing great room with more natural light. It was a smart green choice that fit their lifestyle, but it also looked to the future, when the home would be competing for buyers on the open market.

The fact that you're *greenovating* is a smart preparation for the day you shift from homeowner to home seller. While some projects may not seem like a big deal, making improvements like adding low-flow fixtures in the bathrooms will be appreciated by potential buyers. There are many ways to add value to a home. The best way to ensure your improvements provide payoff potential is to ask your real estate agent for advice. Markets vary, so ask which types of green features are in demand in your market.

2. Keep your climate in mind

North Carolina builder Marcus Renner has a story he likes to tell about the super-green clients who approached him about building an Earthship home in Ashville. An Earthship home is half-submerged and built of rammed earth and recycled tires. It's designed to function in harmony with the environment—a *desert* environment, that is. In arid climates, like New Mexico, their south-facing windows can absorb the heat of the sun during the day, and the dense, heavy walls radiate the heat during the cool desert nights—passive heating in action. It's a brilliant, high-efficiency design for an intended habitat. However, in damp, forested North Carolina, as Renner quickly ascertained, it's less-than-optimal. But his clients insisted on it, so he moved forward.

As Renner predicted, the trouble began almost immediately. The submerged dwelling hit all sorts of groundwater problems. So did the flat roof, which wasn't designed to withstand heavy rain or snow. Unglazed windows leaked much of the heat. Consequently, with the systems in need of frequent overhauls, it was not a good financial value.

We recommend thinking hard about what features will get the most use in your climate. A radiant floor heating system doesn't make much sense in Mobile,

Alabama, where it will only run a couple months a year. Homeowners in the North may want to skip the super, high-efficiency air conditioner and invest instead in sealing and insulation. No matter where you live, there are few green upgrades for which the payback period, also called a cost-benefit analysis, is the same. So do your homework: Ask experts for help in determining which projects are most appropriate for your climate zone.

3. Get more for less

Rest assured, not every green investment needs to be the newest green product on the market. In fact, creatively recycled features are some of the most sustainable options. Did you know that you can purchase decking made out of plastic grocery bags and carpet derived from old soda bottles?

Reusing materials is another green choice worth exploring. Portland remodeler Pat Lando is one shining example of someone who knows how to get more out of less in a home. He carefully re-used virtually all the original components of the 1961 ranch home he remodeled.

"All the doors, all the casework are going back in," he says. "The masonry chimney was ground up for subbase. There's a small amount of hardwood floors that we couldn't use, but that went to someone else's home. So basically, only two dumpsters of material left the site, and one of those was wood being ground up for mulch."

In a world of *"less is more"*, Lando clearly shows that the greenest thing may not be the greenest *new* thing. It might just be the thing you already own.

4. Embrace the payback principle

One of the best things about green improvements is that many of them will pay back through increased energy efficiency. Compact fluorescent lightbulbs are a great example: a $3.50 bulb lasts ten times longer and uses 75 percent less energy than an incandescent bulb. The net result: The compact fluorescent "pays" you about $30 over the life of the bulb. This principle can help you prioritize potential investments.

Payback Period

$$\frac{\text{Total cost of an improvement}}{\text{Estimated cost savings per year}} = \text{Payback Period}$$

Figure 4 – The payback period is the total cost of an improvement divided by the estimated cost savings per year.

According to the U.S. Department of Energy, about 14 percent of an average home's energy costs go to heating water. That said, an efficient hot water heater, such as an Energy Star model, would start paying you back sooner than, say, a more energy-efficient dishwashing machine, which typically accounts for about 2.5 percent of energy, according to the Boston-based Consortium for Energy Efficiency. If you absolutely have to choose between them, upgrade your water heater. In the kitchen, your refrigerator is a much higher priority than a new stove. The U.S. Department of Energy cites the fridge as one of the biggest energy consumer in the home, second only to the HVAC unit.

The payback principle is a smart consideration when you're considering high-dollar investments, such as solar panels or wind turbines. However, there are many great options that can reduce your utility costs and/or lower your carbon footprint. We know that the payback principle can be hard to calculate, because different improvements have different payback lengths, based on factors such as cost of the feature, price of the utilities, how and when you run the feature, and so on. Plus, many of your upgrades—sustainably harvested wood floors, for example—won't pay you any dollars until you sell your home for a premium to a buyer who can appreciate the value. Here's another way to think about it: If a green project is really important to you for nonmonetary reasons, then the payback principle may be less important to you. The true payback might be a cleaner conscience and a better home environment for you to enjoy.

5. Take advantage of potential rebates and incentives

Many states, provinces, and cities are willing to reward your environmental responsibility by offering rebates and incentives for replacing inefficient appliances and fixtures with high-performing new ones.

Depending on where you live, you could get an incentive to do the following:

- Purchase water-conserving appliances and low-flow plumbing fixtures.

- Add solar CPV panels, insulation, or efficient windows and doors.

- Replace grass with drought-tolerant landscaping.

Do your homework early in the planning process so you don't lose your chance for a great rebate check. Ask your real estate agent for advice. If you live in the United States, visit www.dsireusa.org, the Database of State Incentives for Renewables and Efficiency. In Canada, visit www.oee.nrcan.gc.ca/corporate/incentives.cfm or www.ec.gc.ca for information about energy and efficiency rebates.

6. Weigh now vs. later

Part of the planning process involves considering your long-term plans for your home. You don't have to make every improvement today. Even if you're stripping a home down to the studs, there may still be features that don't make sense—or cents—to add right now. Your professional team can help develop your game plan.

Architect Ron Wickman asks, "Maybe you don't want to add all the bells and whistles today, but can you do things that will make it easier to add bells and whistles four or five years down the road?" When he added a second story to his home, he designed the room with wiring for the solar panels he hopes to one day affix to his roof. Again, this not only saves money, it gets back to one of the fundamental principles of green living, which is designing adaptable spaces that will serve you for a lifetime.

Much of your green thinking will depend on your priorities, which we cover in the next chapter. So let's get moving. Let's go green your home!

CHAPTER 2:
FOUR STEPS TO GREENING YOUR HOME

Synergy—the bonus that is achieved when things work together harmoniously.

MARK TWAIN

UNDERSTANDING THE GREENING PROCESS

When you're ready to have a greener home, the likely challenge is not knowing where to start. At its core, creating a greener home is just like any other process: It involves a step-by-step approach to getting the job done. We're going to help you begin that process in this chapter. We've identified four key steps for greening your home—whether you are greenovating your existing home or buying a home with green potential.

Four Steps to Greening Your Home

Step 1.   Clarify your green priorities.

Step 2.   Create your green team.

Step 3.   Build your green project list.

Step 4.   Turn your project list into a plan of action.

In this chapter, we'll explore steps 1 and 2 of the Green Your Home process: Clarify your green priorities and introduce you to the team of professionals who can help you. Step 3, building your green project list, is the core focus of this book, so we've dedicated three chapters to building green action items for each home zone: We'll look at actions for the inside zone in chapter 3; actions for the systems zone in chapter 4; and actions for the outside zone in chapter 5. In chapter 6, we'll walk you through step 4, the final step, in which you'll organize your green project lists into a plan of action. We'll show you how to choose action items for maximum success.

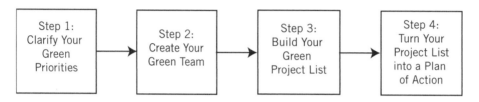

Figure 5 – Four steps to greening your home.

STEP 1: CLARIFY YOUR GREEN PRIORITIES

The process of greening your home starts with getting clear on your priorities. Yes, those same priorities we first introduced in chapter 1: being healthy, money-smart, and sustainable. The goal of this step is to determine the green priority that's most important to you. That is, are your green needs based on health concerns and comfort? Or maybe saving money and greater energy efficiency are top of mind? Or is it your focus on conservation and sustainability that drives your thinking? Like many people, you might find all three priorities important, but to varying degrees.

Achieving clarity on your green priorities will help bring you closer to your green home goals and being clear about your highest priority will bring order to your improvement plans. Why? Because you will take on multiple projects in a sequence over the life of your home ownership journey. You need a starting point, and a project that aligns with your highest priority should be your first order of business. So think about why green matters most to you. Later, in step 3 of the process, you'll make a list of projects. Then, with your priorities identified, you'll be able to narrow your wish list down to the smartest and most effective greenovation projects for you and your home.

The Three Green Priorities

1. A Healthy Home
2. A Money-Smart Home
3. A Sustainable Home

Figure 6 – Determining your green priorities is a simple way to organize your thinking around greening your home.

Take a moment to ask yourself what greening your home will ultimately accomplish for you, your family, and the many friends and visitors who come to your home. What will it mean to the future buyer of your home many years from now? Will your greener home provide peace of mind because it ensures great air quality? Will it offer cost savings from its terrific energy-efficient features? Or does it make a bold statement about living lightly on the planet? To help you find your answers, here's a quick review of the three green priorities in the order that most homeowners prioritize them.

Green Priority No. 1: A Healthy Home

Ralph Waldo Emerson wrote that "the first wealth is health." So it should come as no surprise that mold allergies, chemical sensitivities, asthma, and plain old common sense are all motivations that drive people toward cleaner indoor air. If your green passion begins with a healthy home, prioritize learning about common pollutants so that you can recognize, test, and rid your home of them. Give both passive and spot ventilation a try to keep the air circulating in an optimal way. You'll also choose furnishings and finishes free of toxic chemicals and fumes. In the end, you want a clean, comfortable, and healthy indoor environment: One that gives you peace of mind and promotes good health.

Green Priority No. 2: A Money-Smart Home

Many consumers, builders and agents point to spikes in energy prices as fueling the interest in greener buildings. Simply understanding how you use energy in your home is a solid first step to a money-smart home. Other considerations include installing a digital thermostat, ensuring you have a right-sized HVAC unit, and tightening your building envelope with proper insulation, energy-efficient windows, and weather stripping. Your savings can go through the roof if you factor location into the decision—that is, if you choose a home that minimizes your need to drive every day to work, shop, or run errands.

Green Priority No. 3: A Sustainable Home

Some people want to go green for the same reason others volunteer at animal shelters or donate money to worthy causes—they simply feel it's the right thing to do. Depending on the issues you care about most, there are many ways your home can contribute to a better world. A water-conserving landscape, a habitat-enhancing backyard, and an edible garden of your own are all sustainable considerations. Communicating these passions to your agent and team of green experts will help you get the most out of your green improvement experience.

WHAT DOES GREEN REALLY MEAN?

PRIORITY	GREEN IMPROVEMENT IDEAS
Healthy	1. Interior finishes like hardwood floors and low-VOC paints 2. Exhaust fans in the bathroom and kitchen to reduce moisture 3. Plants throughout the home to help clean the air 4. DIY testing kits for pollutants like mold and radon 5. Carbon monoxide sensors and top-of-the-line air filters
Money Smart	1. Energy-efficient appliances 2. A right-sized, optimally designed HVAC system 3. Passive heating and cooling features 4. A tight building envelope that conserves conditioned air 5. A right-sized home with a smaller footprint
Sustainable	1. Organic interior finishes like wood, cork, or stone 2. Rainwater collection system and storage cistern 3. A great organic vegetable garden and compost system 4. Low-flow showerheads, faucets, and toilets 5. A native-landscaped yard with xeriscape features

Figure 7

These can be examples of how a priority translates into an action item. Action items will be explored in detail in chapters 3–5.

STEP 2: CREATE YOUR GREEN TEAM

It's time to introduce you to the team of experts that will help you on your green journey. We know that there's so much to think about as you look to green your home that it can be overwhelming. And it's important to know that you aren't alone on this home improvement adventure. Your team of experts can explain your options and the type of commitment each potential green improvement project might entail. They can also guide you through unknown territory as well, such as related green improvements. There are a variety of options that may never have occurred to you about any specific project, but are obvious to the experts. Keep in mind, they do this work day in and day out.

Your needs may be relatively simple, requiring nothing more than a series of do-it-yourself projects you'll tackle solo or with friends and relatives as your time and budget allow. On the other hand, if you have leak testing and ductwork to do, rooms that require significant renovation, or the creation of more space in mind, the process of getting there will take a little more planning and the help of skilled professionals. Turning your priorities into a definite plan of action will be a team effort. So whether you have a good sense of what green features you'd like or no idea at all, your team of experts can help move you forward from action to satisfaction.

So who are the players on your green improvement team? We've found that most projects can involve five primary sources of expertise: your real estate agent, general contractors, skilled tradespeople, architects and design-build professionals, and eco-consultants.

The Five Sources of Green Expertise

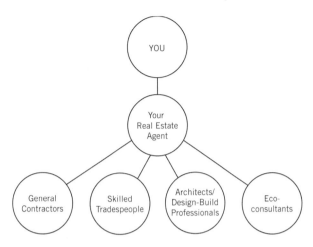

1. **Your Real Estate Agent** – the expert who can help get you into a high-potential green home, who can counsel you on the green improvements that matter most for potential future buyers, and who can connect you to a network of professionals who can tackle the improvements that add the most value in your marketplace.

2. **General Contractors** – the experts who help plan, supervise and guarantee the work, while bringing up-to-the-minute knowledge of construction costs that will impact your budget, and who have access to a network of specialists.

3. **Skilled Tradespeople** – the skilled professionals who tackle specific projects such as carpenters, painters, plumbers, as well as many other trades.

4. **Architects or Design-Build Professionals** – the experts on designing spaces that fit your needs.

5. **Eco-Consultants** – the experts who investigate and test your air quality, energy efficiency, and sustainability and make improvement recommendations.

Figure 8 – The Green Your Home adventure is a team effort. Don't go it alone!

Not everyone will need all the experts listed in figure 8. If you're handy, you may be your own contractor. Or, if all you're doing is installing new floors, you can skip the architect or design-build professional and hire skilled tradespeople to do the installation. Then again, it's always good to understand your options for when the need presents itself. Use the following descriptions to help you decide who will best complete your team.

1. Your Real Estate Agent

There's no one more skilled in helping find you a home with green potential or connecting you to proven home-improvement experts than your real estate agent. Think of your agent as a consultant—one who helps find the home you desire and helps you connect to the team of experts who can help you meet your goals. This is especially true if your agent has taken specialized training to become an expert in green real estate. Agents are not only your trusted resource for any issues pertaining to your home, they are also market experts who understand value. Great agents consider ongoing advice about all things home-related an integral part of their "service for a lifetime" philosophy.

> ### Important Questions to Ask Your Agent
> 1. Can you help me find the professionals who specialize in making green home improvements?
> 2. Can you help me identify homes with green features or green potential?

2. General Contractors

The experienced general contractor (GC) takes responsibility for the whole improvement project. The GC is one of the more expensive experts you might use, but you can count on them to bring a high degree of accountability to the construction process. They are experts at improving homes and will handle all the challenging tasks associated with the construction process, from managing the materials, people, and budget to solving problems on the fly. The advantage of using a GC is that they reduce your risk and carry the responsibility for a project. Rules vary from province to province and state to state, but GCs are often required to be bonded to guarantee you protection for any projects they take on. If you're unsure, just ask the GC to provide proof they're bonded.

3. Skilled Tradespeople

Skilled tradespeople are contractors such as masons, carpenters, painters, plumbers, electricians, heating and cooling system professionals, landscaping experts, and many others. They're a good choice if you have a straightforward need and know exactly what it will take to fulfill it. For example, if you want to replace an old carpet with FSC-certified hardwood floors and simply need someone to install them, then ask your real estate agent to refer you to a professional contractor. If you prefer to handle it on your own, you might check online resources to locate specialized, local contractors with the technical skills you need. But be sure to check their references before signing any contract.

Take extra care when choosing a specialist to work on your mechanical systems, such as the heating and cooling units and any related insulation or ductwork. Green homes need to perform, so quality installation is essential. Energy Star, the U.S. Department of Energy program, and its Canadian counterpart, the Office of Energy Efficiency, encourage home energy efficiency and offer resources for homeowners and contractors. If your province, state, or municipality has a green building program, it may include listings of contractors and home improvement professionals.

Tips for Hiring a Great Professional

When working with a general contractor or specialized tradesperson, do the following:

1. Ask your agent, family, friends, or coworkers for a recommendation—and ask why they recommend that person.
2. Look for experts who are certified or licensed and can offer references.
3. Ask to see examples of their work.
4. When seeking bids for work, always get three to compare and contrast.
5. Use a contract to establish mutual expectations and ensure satisfaction.

---

4. Architects or Design-Build Professionals

Architects can provide in-depth thinking when your improvement plans call for redesigning living space, designing an addition, or creating an outdoor space. They do not come cheap. Generally, architects will charge an hourly fee or a percentage of the total job price. However, working with architects who are trained to treat design as a distinct phase requiring many drafts and refinements is a good way to ensure you think through all your options—a nice check on the urge to blindly jump in and start working. It's also the best way to come up with an amazing, innovative design that fulfills your needs.

Working with an architect is traditionally a two-stage process. First, you go through a step-by-step design stage where you consider and refine options. Take your time! Now is the time to ask "what if?" rather than after contractors are already pounding and pouring. After your plans are finalized, the architect typically seeks bids from a general contractor to manage and execute the process. While your architect will have a general sense of building costs in your market, you won't know for sure until the bids arrive.

Uncertainty about costs is one of the reasons some people sometimes skip the architect in favor of a design-build contractor. In this process, you work directly with a builder, who probably has a draftsman and engineer on staff, to develop your plans based on the builder's real-world expertise and up-to-the-minute cost of projects. Another reason people like to go the route of design-build pros is that they are usually less expensive than architects. However, the design builder may not draw up plans in as extensive detail and may not have the same creativity as someone trained to develop innovative solutions to building challenges. If you choose the design-build path, make sure you know exactly the type of expertise the firm offers and take extra care when reviewing examples of their work.

A "blended" approach is working through an integrated design-build process, which is basically design build with an architect. This teamwork approach offers the best of all worlds—the architect is there to think big and creatively, while the builder offers practical feedback on the cost and feasibility of various options. This is how Edmonton, Alberta, architect Ron Wickman encourages his clients to work. Once he has developed a basic plan and a list of features and finishes that fulfills their dreams, he brings in a contractor who can be the "voice of reason" to refine the client's list.

"As you're building, you have to balance what you want and how much money you have to execute," says Ron. "Clients will dream, and I'll help them dream, but try my best to be a voice of reason. I'm not always aware of what the current price of construction is—as we start to design, something may be one price, and a year later it's 24 percent more expensive. That's where a contractor is so valuable, in keeping us aware of the true costs involved and helping the client make the best choices. Do we do a green roof and maybe sacrifice the flooring? Or maybe the other way around?"

As you're assembling your team, make sure it includes everyone you want involved from the get-go. If your sister or uncle is going to have a say in your design decisions, the time to get their opinion is during the brainstorming, not afterward. And remember, it's okay to do a hundred versions of the design, but once you've decided on a plan, stick with it. Nothing drives up costs more than "pointitecture"—going to the work site, pointing, and saying, "You know, I think maybe the door would look nice over *there*."

5. Eco-Consultants

If healthy, money smart, and sustainable are your priorities, then these professionals, which we call eco-consultants, are your experts. These specialized professionals are trained to offer expertise that will match your priorities. They address health issues from air quality to comfort and even chemical sensitivities, just to name a few. They also know what money smart means—they are energy raters, energy auditors, and lighting designers. And you can bet they deal with sustainability too, as experts in xeriscaping, solar and wind-power systems, and rainwater collection. Many are certified, which ensures you have improvements that are truly green. Eco-consultants offer yet another level of talent and expertise to help you on your green improvement journey.

Tips for Hiring a Great Green Professional

When working with a general contractor or specialized tradesperson, do the following:

1. Bring your list of priorities and pictures of features and design elements you like. Be prepared to talk about why you like them and why they're important to you.
2. Approach the conversation with strong ideas about what you'd like in your home, and keep a flexible approach as to how you might meet those needs.
3. Ask what "green" means to your architect or builder. Have enough of a sense of what green means to you to understand if they have the expertise you need.
4. Remember, you'll be spending a lot of time with this person making very expensive decisions. Confidence and trust are critical!

Some experts may have less or more green expertise. If you know the best general contractor in the world, but that individual is light on green expertise, don't despair. It's not unusual for builders and architects to consult with specialists like eco-consultants themselves. When Gary Keller built his ranch, he hired a great builder and an architect who knew a lot about building green. But even with their combined experience, they sought out a specialist in rainwater collection systems.

You're Not on This Green Journey Alone

An important point to remember is that throughout the Green Your Home process, you can look to your real estate agent for guidance and support. Why your agent? Because there's no better choice when it comes to identifying green potential, value, and local expertise. So, if you don't yet own a home—or you own and desire to trade up to a home with better green features—ask your agent for advice that's relevant to your local market. For example, you may own a starter home in an excellent neighborhood that suits your needs perfectly. In this case, it might make sense to stay in that starter home and turn it into a polished green gem. Then again, the work and cost necessary to pull off an extensive, expensive green transformation might make moving to another home a better option. Let your agent guide you, and trust that he or she is acting as a fiduciary to put your best interests first (and to always remind you of what those interests are).

DANIELA AND ERIC'S STORY: LESSONS IN TEAMWORK

Daniela Bell and Eric Foster were still living in Indiana when they began to put together a plan for relocating to St. Paul, Minnesota. Their real estate agent helped them find a great new home. It was about 1,800 square feet—plenty of space, with an old Victorian charm they liked. But the kitchen and bathroom were badly in need of an update, and the whole house was too dark. To Daniela and Eric, remodeling was a welcome adventure. And since they wanted a home they could improve through green updates anyway, embracing the changes they needed to make was an easy decision.

Daniela and Eric began by working with an architect who understood their tastes and specialized in green renovations. In early meetings, they shared magazine clippings and described the look and functionality they were after. Daniela had been wowed by tankless hot water heaters in Europe and was interested in cork floors, which she found appealing. The conversation included plenty of ideas about how she and Eric intended to use their space. "Michael [the architect] asked a lot of good questions about what kind of things we do in the kitchen; how often we're there," explained Daniela. "He was trying to get a sense of how we'd use the space." Finally, they discussed strategies for going green. Daniela and Eric had taken a very smart first step: They knew they wanted a custom kitchen in their new home, so they worked with their agent to choose a house with an out-of-date kitchen they could tear out and replace, guilt-free. Michael helped them develop a plan to get more out of their existing kitchen and bath space. He helped them fill it with new energy-efficient appliances and fixtures and hip, sustainable finishes. Bringing natural light into the kitchen required a whole bank of new windows. So they opted for energy-conserving, double-paned windows that maximized available daylight.

Some of their other green ideas were put on hold until later. The existing hot water heater, for example, was only a few years old. It didn't make sense to replace it immediately with a more efficient tankless unit, as the energy-saving potential would be canceled out by the waste of throwing away a perfectly good heater. Other ideas went into the "to do later" file because of costs. For instance, many of the leaky old windows stayed because Eric and Daniela just didn't have the budget to replace them all. "We'd come up with ideas but realize we'd need to tackle them down the road in phase two or three," says Eric. "We'll do more over the years, depending on how long we stay here."

Daniela and Eric ended up with a smart, water-conserving, space-maximizing bathroom with a custom mountain scene in handmade tile on their wall. And their now one-of-a-kind kitchen allows them to stir and chop without bumping elbows on a remnant granite counter that swoops through the space. The design was not what they'd envisioned going in; in fact, it was even better. They credit the success of their project to their relationship with their architect and to two things in particular: They trusted his understanding of their taste and they trusted that his values matched their own. "As we were brainstorming, Michael would come up with some really crazy ideas, ones we thought were cool because we were a really good match in terms of liking a distinct modern design—and the use of color," says Daniela.

You don't absolutely need to hire an architect or design-build professional who shares your tastes or your particular passion for green-minded practices. In fact, you may find the scope of your green improvement projects don't call for high-level expertise or an expensive budget at all. However, if you do choose to work with a team of green renovation professionals, the collaboration process will be much richer and the ultimate outcome more satisfying if they act as true partners. Together, you and your team can dream and, ultimately, turn those dreams into a green home.

The most important thing to remember when embarking on the adventure of greening your home is that it's an ongoing process and it won't be accomplished overnight. However, like Daniela and Eric, by having a concrete understanding of what you hope to accomplish in your home and the team that can help accomplish it, you too can achieve a green home in a simple way that suits you perfectly.

READY FOR ACTION

Congratulations! You've worked your way through steps 1 and 2 of the Green Your Home process. At this point, you've clarified your priorities. You also have identified your team of experts, the professionals you may need to call upon while on your green adventure. In step 3, which we cover in the next three chapters, we'll move into the three zones of the home. We're going to take a closer look at the inside, systems, and outside zones of your home. We'll revisit our model and share projects tied to each priority that are most important in each of these zones. The first zone we'll look at is the inside zone, where health is our highest priority.

CHAPTER 3:
THE INSIDE ZONE

Water, air, and cleanness are the chief articles in my pharmacy.

NAPOLEON BONAPARTE

SARA'S STORY: A HEALTHY HOME COMES FIRST

For most of her life, Sara Alvarado didn't give much thought to indoor air quality. She never suffered from allergies or chemical sensitivities, and she didn't mind the smell of new paint. "I was a typical '80s girl," she says, thinking back to those carefree days of aerosol hairspray. "I didn't think about global warming or other environmental issues. I figured we have been around for thousands of years, so we'll be fine."

The '80s girl grew up and became a real estate agent in Madison, Wisconsin. As she was expecting her second child, a boy, she and her husband bought the perfect new home to grow in together as a family. It was a spacious two-story, located in a district with a great Spanish-immersion charter school, and it had a huge backyard for the kids to run around in. The Alvarados closed on the home, had all new paint and carpet put in, and moved in two weeks later.

Sara's son Leo was born in the winter. She brought him home to her warm, cozy house and kept the Wisconsin cold safely outside with tightly sealed windows. Soon, however, Leo began to cough. After a long, grueling winter of doctor's appointments and wheezing, he was diagnosed with viral asthma. "That started our passion," says Sara. "When you have a sick kid, you want to do all you can for him."

The doctors had one answer: prescription drugs. But Sara began to wonder about all the smells in her bright, clean home. She hired an indoor air quality specialist who quickly recommended a series of changes to keep the air in Leo's tiny lungs as clean and pure as possible. She started regularly opening windows to air out the pollutants emanating from the new paint and carpets. She opened the heavy shades over the windows, where condensation from the cold windows was accumulating and molding. She replaced all her cleaning products with nontoxic varieties and bought a mechanical air cleaner that scrubbed the pollutants and irritants out of the air coming through the vents. "The doctors made it sound like all you can do is get inhalers, but we learned there's a lot you can do," says Sara. "The more research we did, the more empowered we felt."

And the more they did, the more Leo's health improved. On one fall day when Leo was three years old, Sara was able to report that he had been free of asthma attacks for the last four months. Their journey to health had not only changed Sara's home, it transformed her entire outlook on life.

"I learned so much," says Sara. "I now realize that these changes also help the planet. Our next mission is to start focusing on and raising money to help improve the air quality and energy efficiency of our local schools."

Now, we want to take you on a similar journey in this chapter, one that leaves you feeling empowered to take control of the healthiness of your inside home zone.

THE INSIDE ZONE: HEALTH IS YOUR 20 PERCENT

Being healthy is probably one of the most important priorities you have, especially inside your home. Why? The answer is simple. As you may recall, you spend more time inside than you do anyplace else. In fact, more than 80 percent of your nonwork and noncommuting time is spent inside your home. Being in a healthy indoor environment is too important a consideration to ignore.

When we talk about health in the inside zone, much of the conversation will be about air. Even though we can't see it, air is a supportive element that has a huge impact on the health of our inside zone. Actually, an average adult takes more than 14,000 breaths and inhales and exhales more than 11,000 liters* (that's about 3,000 gallons) of air in a single day! Babies breathe even more frequently—taking, on average, more than 43,000 breaths in a day. Over the course of many years, this adds up to hundreds of millions of breaths. We do the majority of our breathing inside our homes, so it's worth making sure that the air we breathe there is healthy.

That's where we come in—to help you do just that. While we're ready to guide you with ways to be healthy in the inside zone of your home, we'll also give you the advice and tools you'll need to make your inside zone money smart and

---

* http://health.howstuffworks.com/human-body/systems/respiratory/question98.htm

sustainable. As you turn the pages, use our suggestions to create your own to-do list of the action items you'd like to take on. Join us now on the first leg of your Green Your Home adventure!

PROJECT 1: MASTER LIST FOR THE INSIDE ZONE

PRIORITY	ACTION ITEMS

Healthy	1. Bring Fresh Air Inside
	   • *Use Passive Ventilation*
	   • *Use Spot Ventilation*
	
	2. Get to Know Your Pollutants
	   • *Understand Radon*
	   • *Understand Mold*
	   • *Understand Dust*
	   • *Understand Lead-Based Paint*
	   • *Understand Asbestos*
	   • *Understand Volatile Organic Compounds (VOCs)*
	   • *Understand Combustion Gas*
	
	3. Test for Possible Pollutant Sources in Your Home
	   • *Use Your Senses*
	   • *Get a DIY Test Kit*
	   • *Have Your Home Professionally Tested*
	
	4. Keep Pollutants Out
	   • *Keep Gases Vented to the Outside*
	   • *Keep Your Home Dry*
	   • *Keep Your Home Nontoxic*
	   • *Keep Your Home Clean*
	
	continued

PRIORITY	ACTION ITEMS (CONTINUED)

Money Smart	5. Improve Your Lighting Design
	    • *Embrace Natural Lighting*
	    • *Choose Smart Artificial Lighting Sources*
	6. Boost Energy Efficiency
	    • *Sometimes You Don't Need Power*
	    • *Take Control of Your Phantom Load*
	    • *Make Your Appliances Perform*

Sustainability	7. Get Water Wise
	    • *Choose Water-Efficient Appliances*
	    • *Change How You Use Water Indoors*
	8. Add Smart, Sustainable Interior Design Features
	    • *Choose Sustainable Paint Finishes*
	    • *Choose Sustainable Flooring*

Figure 9

STEP 3: BUILD YOUR GREEN PROJECT LIST

In the last chapter, we covered steps 1 and 2 of the Green Your Home process. Step 1 answered the question of why you want to green your home and gave you clarity on the priorities that drive most decisions—being healthy, money smart, and sustainable. Step 2 informed you of who can help you green your home, experts such as real estate agents, general contractors, skilled trade professionals, architects and design-build pros, and finally, eco-consultants.

Now comes step 3, when you can begin to build your project list. Step 3 will extend through each of the next three chapters, which address the three home zones: inside, systems, and outside. Remember, your project list is the hard work *before* the hard work! In the last chapter of this book, you'll move on to Step 4: Turn Your Project List Into a Plan of Action.

With the action items we are about to describe to you, you'll see that everything inside your home is interconnected, not just a collection of isolated features. "If you think green means going on a green shopping spree, you are mistaken," says Colleen McLean, who works with a team of home-performance evaluators in Los Angeles, California. "Green requires following the laws of physics." We designed this book so that the action items are complementary and budget conscious. You don't have to do them all, but if you do, the items will work well together. So keep this in mind when you take on improvements in each of the zones of your home.

We're now ready to tackle your home's inside zone. We encourage you to take notes as you go. Pick the action items that make sense and dream up all the possible ways to maximize your health and comfort inside your home, not to mention, make some improvements that will save you money and improve your sustainability by conserving resources in the process. Feel free to work in this book; write down your ideas and put a star by your favorite items! This is a critical step on the Green Your Home adventure, so let's get moving.

A HEALTHY INSIDE ZONE

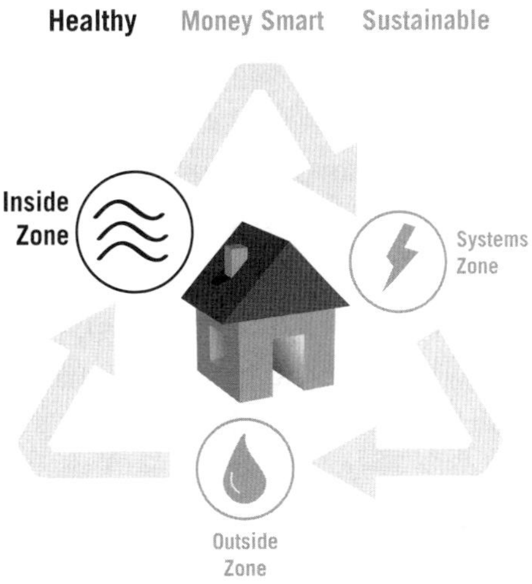

Say the words "air pollution" and you probably think of a smokestack spewing a dark, dirty cloud into the atmosphere, or rush-hour congestion on a smoggy Los Angeles highway. You definitely don't think about the favorite rooms of your home. However, research conducted by the Environmental Protection Agency has shown that you are more likely to breathe polluted air inside your home than outside—even in Los Angeles. It's a scary thought! We believe that our homes should be our safe, healthy,

Figure 10 – Clean air is one of the keys to a healthy inside zone.

secure retreats from the world outside. Unfortunately, many homes simply aren't up to that task. It's far too common to build, improve, or remodel a home without giving serious thought to the way it will affect the health of its residents. Poor ventilation, construction mistakes, and even normal paints, sealants, and finishes all add to the pollution potential in a typical home.

Given how much time we know people spend indoors every day, anything less than clean air is a problem. More troubling is the fact that the number of families like Sara Alvarado's is rapidly growing. No one knows exactly why, but the number of Americans with asthma and allergies has more than doubled since 1980, according to a report published by the Air Pollution and

Respiratory Health Branch of the National Center for Environmental Health. Some people also suffer from multiple chemical sensitivities (MCS), a chronic condition caused by exposure to certain types of chemicals. But even if you don't know anyone with a medical condition that makes clean indoor air an absolute necessity, you may still be one of the millions of people who believe that providing the cleanest, safest, most nontoxic home possible is simply the smart thing to do. Fortunately, the growing interest in safer homes has made it easy to find the professionals and products you need to make your home the healthy haven you deserve.

We've already established that to create a healthy inside zone, you need to focus on action items relating to your air quality first. Start by looking in the mirror and asking yourself, "Am I doing what I need to do to keep my home free of dangers and dirt?" As a simple example, do you have mats outside your doors for wiping your shoes? Throughout this book, we encourage you to apply simple solutions, the low-hanging fruit that can green your home at little expense or inconvenience. Now, let's take a look at four action items to improve the health of your inside zone.

Four Action Items for Making Your Inside Zone Healthier

Action Item (1) Bring fresh air inside.

Action Item (2) Get to know your pollutants.

Action Item (3) Test for possible pollutant sources in your home.

Action Item (4) Keep pollutants out.

ACTION ITEM 1: BRING FRESH AIR INSIDE

Just like you, your home has to breathe; unlike you, however, your home does not always breathe by itself. You need to bring the fresh air inside and you can do so by opening your windows regularly. Even the most advanced, well-conceived green homes need help. Homeowner Jeff Miner learned this lesson the hard way. He was delving deep into green, decades before it became a worldwide trend.

Jeff built his dream green home in the mountains above Lake Tahoe in 1980. Solar energy was his passion. He built a home designed for passive solar with abundant south-facing windows and installed only a single wood-burning stove for heat. Obsessed with efficiency, he built what was essentially an airtight bubble, a home with 8-inch-thick insulated walls and windows sealed with foam insulation.

Things didn't turn out quite as planned, however. His daughter, who has the autoimmune disease lupus, started getting respiratory problems from the woodstove's fumes. His wife, who also has chemical sensitivity, was getting headaches from the off-gassing chemicals released by their new carpets. So Miner brought in an eco-consultant, an air quality expert, to analyze the air quality in his house. "I had a blower-door test done to check how tight the house was," Jeff says. "The inspector said, 'Your house is over the top. You need some air infiltration.' I had built it so well I forgot that I needed natural ventilation."

Simply put, Jeff's home needed to breathe. Jeff then applied the same care he took in efficient design to the air quality of his home. He installed exhaust fans, and he regularly opens windows on either side of the home to ensure cross-ventilation. In the kitchen, he replaced the gas-powered stove with an electric one. For heat, he replaced the wood-burning stove with a gas model directly vented to the outside. He bought several indoor air cleaners and leaves them running. He discovered he had high radon levels, so he sealed his house from the dangerous gases. With his home now properly ventilated, his wife and daughter feel healthy inside their home, and Jeff has peace of mind.

"The people with chemical sensitivities are the canaries in the coal mine, but those fumes aren't doing any of us any good," Jeff says. "You want to avoid things that force your immune system into high gear."

Jeff illustrates the balancing act of a high-performance home: It must be tight, but it also must be able to breathe right. As we shared with you earlier, good ventilation can be as basic as opening up a few windows on opposite sides and letting a cross breeze flow through your home. Well-placed mechanical ventilation units also can go a long way to help keep your air in good shape. We recommend you consider the following strategies to bring fresh air into your home.

Green Strategies for Bringing Fresh Air Inside (Action Item 1)
- Green Strategy I: Use Passive Ventilation
- Green Strategy II: Use Spot Ventilation

Green Strategy I: Use Passive Ventilation

If you live in a mild climate, building passive ventilation into your home is a cheap, natural complement to mechanical systems. A single window open to the outside isn't going to cut it. You need cross-ventilation so the breeze actually blows through. Many older homes in warm climates were designed to create interior "breezeways" in the days before air-conditioning was the norm. If you're planning an addition, attention to prevailing breezes in your area or strategic placement for cross-ventilation will deliver long-term comfort at zero additional cost. If you live in an area where breeze is scarce and you have a tall home, you can employ the "chimney effect" to get air flowing through the house. This can be as simple as opening a window on the bottom and top floors. The warm air will flow up and out of the opening near the top of the home, while fresh air flows in downstairs. If you live in a breezy area but there are homes or vegetation blocking the wind, you might consider installing a wind catcher or a turbine ventilator. These features are installed on the roof and channel breezes down and through the house. If you're interested, ask your agent for a referral to a professional.

Green Strategy II: Use Spot Ventilation

In most areas, bathroom and kitchen exhaust fans are required features in a home—don't forget to use them. Bathroom fans are essential to prevent mold and mildew. On the other hand, a kitchen fan will also remove moisture that's generated from simmering foods, as well as the carbon monoxide generated by gas burners. Remember to make sure it vents—it may surprise you, but many of these vents are just for show! If you have an attached garage, a well-placed exhaust fan will draw the car exhaust out before it has a chance to enter your home. Just be sure to let it run for several minutes after you have turned off your car's engine. You can also have your garage exhaust fan synchronized to your garage door. Talk to your agent or ask friends if they can refer a great garage-exhaust-fan service professional.

One reason people fail to run their fans is the noise, so if you're shopping for an exhaust fan, get a quiet one. The sound of bathroom fans is measured by "sone." A sone of under 2.0 is quiet enough that most people won't mind leaving it on; a fan that's rated sone 1.0 will just be a gentle whoosh. As they need to run for about twenty minutes (long enough for most of us to forget about it), installing a timer also helps turn bathroom ventilation into a simple no-brainer.

Passive and spot ventilation are tried-and-true methods for improving indoor air quality and preventing serious problems. It's worth noting that there are also more sophisticated ventilation systems. And because these are complex and mechanical, we'll cover them more thoroughly in chapter 4, which covers the systems zone. Later in the chapter, we'll show you how to test for and eradicate air toxins. Let's now turn to our second action item for improving air quality.

ACTION ITEM 2: GET TO KNOW YOUR POLLUTANTS

Got pollutants? You might. Knowing where to find potential pollutants begins with simply identifying the more common ones. To do this, you must first educate yourself by reading up on the different types of household pollutants that you may find in your home. Our intention is not to overwhelm or frighten you, but instead to arm you with useful information. If you can identify the problem, you can apply the correct solution. So let's meet our pollutants.

Green Strategies for Getting to Know Your Pollutants (Action Item 2)

- Green Strategy I: Understand Radon
- Green Strategy II: Understand Mold
- Green Strategy III: Understand Dust
- Green Strategy IV: Understand Lead-Based Paint
- Green Strategy V: Understand Asbestos
- Green Strategy VI: Understand Volatile Organic Compounds (VOCs)
- Green Strategy VII: Understand Combustion Gas

Green Strategy I: Understand Radon

Radon is an odorless gas that is 100 percent natural. It's also 100 percent deadly. In fact, the Environmental Protection Agency lists radon as the second-leading cause of lung cancer after cigarette smoke in the United States. Radon gas is produced when uranium in the soil breaks down. It enters the home through dirt floors, cracks in the walls, drains and sumps. Almost any home in North America can have a radon problem, particularly if you live over granite bedrock.

Green Strategy II: Understand Mold

Think of the musty smell in that dirt-floor basement where grandma kept the twenty-year supply of pickled beets. Now think of the weird orange scum growing on the shower curtain in your friend's apartment in college. What do the two have in common? They're both places where continuous moisture breeds mold. Many people are allergic to common molds or develop the allergy after living for years in a moldy house—some uncommon molds can also be very dangerous. An out-of-control mold problem cannot only make you sick, if the source is an untreated leak, but it can destroy an entire home.

Green Strategy III: Understand Dust

Dust is not a single thing, but a complex potpourri of tiny bits of . . . well . . . practically anything. From your pet's hair to crumbs from last week's slumber-party s'mores adventure to the tracked-in grit from the driveway. Dust is also a natural habitat for dust mites: the tiny, microscopic insects that share our homes and give some people awful allergies.

Green Strategy IV: Understand Lead-Based Paint

If anyone counters your concern for potential toxins in your home with the old "No one's *proven* it's dangerous. . ." line, we've got three words for them: *lead-based paint*. Before anyone *proved* what we now know to be true—that lead was a potent neurotoxin, even in tiny quantities—it was used in a variety of products and was a key ingredient in practically every gallon of paint slapped on walls from Nova Scotia to New Mexico. If your home was built before 1950, it almost certainly contains lead-based paint; before the mid-80s, it's also highly likely. Stuck to your walls, lead-based paint is not a problem. The second it starts peeling or flaking, it becomes a toxin that puts you and your children at risk of breathing or accidentally ingesting it.

Green Strategy V: Understand Asbestos

The other half of the dynamic duo of "just because we think it's safe now" products is asbestos, which was widely used in structures and insulation until the 1970s. It causes cancer and is now illegal. Like lead-based paint, it's not an issue if it's firmly secured within tile, insulation, or other material. The health risks arise when you remodel, move, or agitate these materials and potentially unleash asbestos dust into your home and lungs. If you have a home that was built before 1980 and you are planning to remodel it, talk with a professional asbestos remediation expert *before* undertaking any work. In Action Item 3, you'll learn how to scope out this potential danger in your own home.

Green Strategy VI: Understand Volatile Organic Compounds (VOCs)

They may sound like something from Star Trek, but VOCs are familiar to us all. VOCs are a fancy name for "fumes," the gases that newly manufactured products continue to release for weeks, months, or even years. Think "new car smell." While many of us rather enjoy the new car smell and its cousins—new home or new furniture smells—our bodies do not. Even if the fumes go away after a few weeks, the hazardous waste from the manufacture of sealants, adhesives and finishes is harder to get rid of. One particularly creepy VOC is formaldehyde, a likely carcinogen that is nevertheless a common ingredient in particleboard and common furnishings, such as cabinetry.

Green Strategy VII: Understand Combustion Gas

In addition to the dangers from your car's exhaust in your garage, there are other gases to be aware of in your home. Your roaring furnace or crackling fireplace may keep your toes toasty and your marshmallows crisp, but also may pose a potential health hazard. A natural by-product of combustion is carbon monoxide, which in high concentrations will prevent your body from absorbing oxygen and can even kill you. If they are not properly ventilated and maintained, furnaces, fireplaces, and hot water heaters are all potential sources of carbon monoxide and other combustion gases.

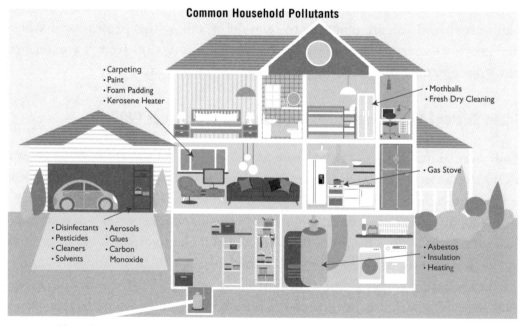

Figure 11 – Almost every room in a typical household has items that can pollute the air.

Green Tips: Minimize Your Pollutant Risk Room by Room

1. In the garage. If your car engine is running, make sure your garage door is open. Allow time for exhaust fumes to ventilate. And if you have the budget for it, install an exhaust fan.

2. In the living areas. When buying furniture and flooring products like carpets, be sure to investigate how the products are made and any harmful chemicals that might off-gas in your home. If you do purchase potentially hazardous products, be sure to open windows and let fresh air in every day.

3. In the bathroom. Use cleaning products that don't contain harmful chemicals. Instead, opt for green cleaning products that use natural solvents, like citrus and vinegar. Use low-VOC caulks to protect against moisture and mold and be sure to run your exhaust fans after showering.

ACTION ITEM 3: TEST FOR POSSIBLE POLLUTANT SOURCES IN YOUR HOME

We hope our list of potential hazards hasn't scared you into trading the home in the burbs for a tent in the woods. It shouldn't. When your home is clean, well-maintained, and functioning properly, it truly can be the refuge you deserve. Your job on this journey is to help get it there—and to keep it there. Now that you're educated about the potential hazards and they are on your list of no-no's, the next action item is to search thoroughly for telltale signs of danger.

Green Strategies, Testing For Possible Pollutant Sources in Your Home (Action Item 3)

- Green Strategy I: Use Your Senses
- Green Strategy II: Get a DIY Test Kit
- Green Strategy III: Have Your Home Professionally Tested

Green Strategy I: Use Your Senses

Imagine you're in the air freshener aisle in the grocery store. You look over the different scents: pine forest, sea breeze, wild flowers, and so forth. There's one you don't see, pure air. The reason is obvious—you can't put the smell of pure air in a can, because it smells like, well, nothing at all. Which brings up our first rule of home air monitoring: If your house smells like something other than mom's apple pie or dad's barbecue chicken, you likely have a problem.

A dusty, musty, moldy, or chemical smell isn't just an annoyance; it's a symptom of an underlying condition that should not be ignored. Your eyes are as important a tool as your nose, so don a face mask and safety goggles and check out your basement and attic—if you have either. Wet spots, moldy spots, and gaps in the ductwork are all possible sources of air pollution. In the home itself, look at the walls for old, peeling paint that may contain lead. And look below your feet. If you're standing on carpet, you're standing on a big playground for dust, particulates, mites, and other unpleasant substances. Your five senses are your first line of defense against mold and dust. But they'll utterly fail you for some of the deadliest indoor pollutants, such as radon or carbon monoxide, which are odorless.

Green Strategy II: Get a DIY Test Kit

Fortunately, for the fearless do-it-yourselfers among us, a multitude of options exist on the market today to test your home for various pollutants. We suggest purchasing simple and inexpensive test kits for radon, carbon monoxide, lead, mold and bacteria, and formaldehyde. These are easy to purchase both online and at home-improvement stores. Your local government may also give testing kits away for free.

When testing for these pollutants yourself, we recommend you file away some information we think you'll find useful. Radon levels may fluctuate based on the weather or atmospheric conditions, so even if you get a safe reading initially, you may want to test again from time to time. Carbon monoxide test kits are especially useful for uncovering this silent killer in kitchens, garages, and near fireplaces, where carbon monoxide can build up to dangerous levels. Home test kits for lead can be used on a variety of products, from walls to silverware, to make sure you aren't inadvertently exposing yourself or your family to this pollutant. Testing for mold and bacteria requires the use of culture plates, like the petri dishes you used in your high school science lab. Most kits come with a handy chart to help you identify the type of mold you might have. Some people also install humidity sensors, which can help monitor dampness and give you an early heads-up on problems that can cause mold. Last, but not least, testing for formaldehyde involves leaving out the test kit for several days and then sending it to a professional lab for analysis.

Green Strategy III: Have Your Home Professionally Tested

Caring for a home is a little like caring for a car: You can check your oil or keep an eye open for funny warning lights on the dashboard, but if you really want to know what's going on under the hood, you should probably bring in a professional mechanic. So this is where your team of experts can come in handy!

Eco-consultants, such as home-performance evaluators or indoor air quality specialists, use fancy equipment to test for various toxic gases, humidity, temperature, ventilation, and other air conditions. They can use infrared cameras to find leaks and water sources.

However technical the tools they use, what air quality specialists and home-performance evaluators can do is give you a detailed diagnosis that will shape your improvement choices. "Before doing any remodel, it's a good idea to test your entire home to understand what the baseline conditions are," says Dan Morris, retired senior air quality consultant at EHSI/Healthy Buildings, Inc., Bellevue, Washington. "Homeowners always say that indoor air quality is at the top of their lists, but it's one of the least understood of all the features you could put in the home."

So, to identify the potential pollutants in your home, there are three things that you need to do. First, use your senses to initially scope out potential problems in your home. If you can smell it or see it, chances are you may have a problem. Next, you can test your home further with a DIY kit, such as a simple radon testing kit that you can buy at many hardware or home-improvement stores. And finally, you can bring in your team of experts and have your home professionally tested. If you have it in your budget, we believe it's well worth the money and peace of mind to have your home professionally tested. As always, ask your agent or friends for a referral—and once you've found a professional, ask them for references.

ACTION ITEM 4: KEEP POLLUTANTS OUT

Dan Morris knows what he's talking about. After inspecting more than 4,000 homes in the Seattle area, he has seen the hazards that poor maintenance, improper construction, and simple neglect can wreak on people's lives. One of his most potent warning stories involves an award-winning green home. The home was only eight years old, but the clients called him in because the whole family was having health problems.

Dan did the usual tests and found high levels of carbon monoxide in his meter. The culprit was instantly clear: an enormous water heater that ran the home's cutting-edge radiant heat system. The gas-powered heater was in a tiny laundry room with no windows, next to a big clothes dryer that vented to the outside. When the dryer ran, the vent to the outside created pressure that sucked the carbon monoxide from the burning gas back down the flue (the heater's exhaust pipe) and into the home. "This was not an indoor air quality problem," says Dan. "It was an indoor air quality disaster. And the architect, the builder, the inspector, and the homeowner had all missed it."

In that situation, the problem was solved by installing mechanical ventilation strong enough to pull the heater's fumes outside rather than allowing them to build up. (We'll discuss mechanical ventilation in more depth in the next chapter on the systems zone.) The tools required to transform a standard home into a pristine green palace will vary depending on your home's original condition and your ultimate vision for your home environment. But there are principles for keeping pollutants out. In particular, you want to apply the following strategies.

Green Strategies for Keeping Pollutants Out (Action Item 4)

- Green Strategy I: Keep Gases Vented to the Outside
- Green Strategy II: Keep Your Home Dry
- Green Strategy III: Keep Your Home Nontoxic
- Green Strategy IV: Keep Your Home Clean

Green Strategy I: Keep Gases Vented to the Outside

Under ideal conditions, your furnace, fireplace, or water heater burns its fuel efficiently and dangerous gases like carbon monoxide flow directly outside through a chimney, duct, or flue. But in many older homes, this ideal ventilation scenario isn't functioning quite like it should. Tight ductwork and carefully sealed ventilation features are your first line of defense against potentially deadly backdrafting. The appliances you choose can also make a difference. If you are buying a furnace, you might want to consider a "direct vent" model, which eliminates the risk of backdrafting by bringing air in and out of the furnace directly from the outside; choosing gas-burning stoves without a continuously burning pilot light takes you another step closer to safety.

As you look to the years ahead, the most important step toward reducing combustion gases is to keep all your appliances maintained annually. An HVAC professional will inspect the flues for rust and soot, make sure that the furnace is operating efficiently, and check that the heat exchanger is in good condition. A cracked heat exchanger will leak gases directly into the duct system, posing a definite danger.

Green Strategy II: Keep Your Home Dry

Damp basements are not the only way that mold-growing moisture builds up in your home. That's something Wanda Zinski knows all too well. When Wanda and her husband were preparing to sell their first home in Utica, New York, they called in an inspector to help them decide what kind of improvements would make it market-ready. What he discovered surprised them. In the attic above their bathrooms, he found black mold growing all over the ceilings. For the entire decade they had been living there, they simply hadn't bothered to run the exhaust fan while they were taking showers, and all that moisture built up and began to rot! The family hired a specialist to clean up the mold before selling, and in their new home they now run the fans daily.

We recommend you protect your family from mold in two ways: Make sure you don't have an existing mold problem, and control moisture sources to keep mold from developing. If you're shopping for a home or if it has been a while since you bought your home, pay attention to see if your inspector is actually getting up in the attic or wriggling around in the crawlspace to look for problems. If he just pokes his head up and shines a flashlight around, you will probably want to double-check, or hire an air quality specialist to check for you. If you have a mold problem, many states and territories require certified contractors to do your improvements for you. We hope, however, that you *don't* have a mold problem and your goal is simply to keep one from developing. If so, there are simple ways to help prevent mold.

Green Tips: How to Prevent Mold

1. Seal it off. Since it is typically damp and cold and an ideal breeding ground for mold, you want to make sure that your basement or crawlspace is sealed off.

2. Make it a habit. Run your bathroom exhaust fan for at least twenty minutes every time you take a shower—installing one with a timer can help.

3. Be vigilant about leaks. Check the caulking around your showers, sinks, tubs, toilets and other moisture sources, and don't ignore damp spots in your ceiling or mysterious puddles that indicate hidden drips.

4. Use the right-sized air conditioner. A right-sized air conditioner is the size that will most thoroughly dehumidify as it cools. The Energy Star website offers square footage charts and usage adjustment calculations that can help you determine the best-sized air conditioner, whether it's a central air unit or window unit, for your space.

5. Monitor your humidity. Install a humidity monitor, also called a hygrometer—if your home's humidity strays too far from the comfortable zone of 50 percent, you may want to consider buying a dehumidifier.

Green Strategy III: Keep Your Home Nontoxic

So far we've been talking about natural sources of pollution—yes, even the loose dog fur under the couch qualifies. What matters most to many green-home owners, however, is the unnatural stuff—the volatile organic compounds (VOCs) and other chemical-rich, factory-produced products that hitch a ride into your home on your shiny new stuff, like a can of paint, a piece of furniture, or your flooring. These items can produce what is known as "off-gassing" or "out-gassing," a process in which a product slowly releases toxic chemical fumes in low concentrations over time.

Fortunately, the high demand for less-toxic alternatives has taken root. And because low-toxin materials yield benefits you can literally feel, we hope you'll take advantage of them. As you are shopping the home-improvement stores or working with your team of experts, look for low- or no-VOC paints, caulks, and sealants certified by the independent nonprofit GreenSeal, an organization that tests to ensure these products have low levels of fumes and do not contain about a dozen particularly dangerous chemicals.

A note of caution: The claim "low VOC" alone isn't enough. A paint may be labeled a low-VOC product and contain up to five times the fumes of a GreenSeal-certified product. If you're really interested in the all-natural, safe-paint product, you can look online and find paints made from a base of milk, beeswax, citrus, and a variety of other nonmanufactured substances.

As in the case of low-VOC products, manufacturers are responding with formaldehyde-free alternatives for particleboard and similar products. Many of these products are also double-duty—instead of grinding up trees to get the "particles" from which the "board" is manufactured, they use post-consumer waste (your old cardboard boxes) or agricultural by-products that otherwise would simply be burnt, like wheat stalks.

Choosing independently certified low- or no-VOC and formaldehyde-free products is one of the easiest and most fun ways to demonstrate your green commitment. However, remember that most of the damage from off-gassing products comes in the early years of their useful lives. After a certain period, even the worst cabinets have off-gassed as much as they're going to. So don't rush out and replace your old wood floors with new bamboo or throw some low-VOC paint on the walls for the sake of your lungs, unless the aesthetic damage they're doing to your eyes compels you to do so.

Green Tips: Ways to Keep Your Inside Zone Nontoxic

1. Watch your VOC levels. Use low-VOC paints, caulks, and sealants certified to the GS-11 standard by GreenSeal.

2. Forget the formaldehyde. Use formaldehyde-free particleboard or fiberboard, preferably manufactured with high recycled content.

3. Au naturel is best. Less is more, so avoid products that have chemical treatments and wear out fast, such as most carpets.

Green Strategy IV: Keep Your Home Clean

Dust is just a fancy word for the tiny bits of the world outside that end up in your home. Short of giving Fluffy the cat a buzz cut, your only real strategy against dust is to keep your place clean. As one seeking green improvements, you can make this task easier or harder on yourself in the years to come depending on the materials you choose. Carpet, for example, holds an enormous amount of crud. The pollutants in dust can be particularly hazardous to young children, who play on the floor and tend to put things in their mouths. We suggest considering alternatives to wall-to-wall carpeting, such as stained concrete, hardwoods, bamboo, or tile floors jazzed up with small area rugs that are easier to clean regularly. Other strategies for ongoing dust management are to use a vacuum with a high-efficiency filter and dust floors, walls, and ceilings with a damp cloth once a week. The Asthma Society of Canada suggests washing your bedding with hot water at least once a week to control dust mites. Because dust mites also love mattresses, which are a little harder to simply toss in the machine, you may also invest in a washable, zippered cover that keeps the dust mites out of your mattress.

Another way to keep your home clean is to use an air cleaner and in-duct filter. A well-designed air cleaner can remove some of the irritating particles from the air you breathe. The right air cleaner—either a portable air cleaning unit or an in-duct filter system—can reduce the amount of allergens in a home's indoor air when used, maintained and replaced regularly. In-duct filters used in your forced-air, HVAC, or furnace system are a simple and inexpensive way to make your air a little cleaner. Both portable and in-duct air cleaners and filters work even better in combination with the other steps already outlined in this chapter—making sure you're bringing in enough fresh, outdoor air and removing the source of pollutants from inside your home. Together these efforts are an effective, proven part of an overall plan to improve your air quality and the health of your inside zone. We'll discuss in-duct filters in greater details in the next chapter, when we cover the systems zone of your home.

Lucky for us, NASA doesn't just study space travel. In fact, several decades of NASA research provides us with a helpful and down-to-earth strategy for maintaining clean air: common houseplants. Positioned throughout the rooms of our homes, with one houseplant for every 150 square feet of home, plants offer a highly effective and affordable way to help improve our indoor air quality. They clear the air of impurities, like formaldehyde, a carcinogen which is commonly found in many products such as particleboard, pressed wood, and carpets. Not only do plants purify the air, they control humidity, absorb carbon dioxide, and provide us with clean, oxygen-rich air. Some plants are better at filtering specific particulates than others. We recommend filling your house with powerful houseplants such as the areca palm, bamboo palm, peace lily, and (our favorite) mother-in-law's tongue. Visit your local nursery to find out what's available and for tips on proper care and lighting conditions for any plants you purchase.

A MONEY-SMART INSIDE ZONE

As we learned in the earlier pages of this book, being money smart is an important priority that can influence the action items you choose to undertake on your green adventure. And when we speak of being money smart, we are mostly referring to efforts that save energy. Here, we'll focus on how you can be money smart by making better choices about your energy in the inside zone. In particular, we'll help you reconsider your lighting design and improve the efficiency of your electronics and appliances. Keep in mind that in the systems zone, which we cover in the next chapter, we'll provide more in-depth guidance on how to maximize energy efficiency throughout your entire home. So, get ready to learn how to make your inside zone as money smart as can be!

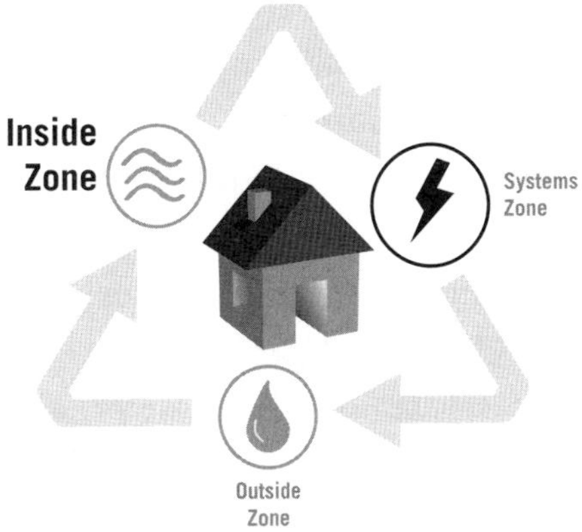

Healthy **Money Smart** Sustainable

Figure 12 – Being money smart in the inside zone means being energy efficient.

Two Action Items for Making Your Inside Zone More Money Smart

Action Item (5)   Improve Your Lighting Design
Action Item (6)   Boost Energy Efficiency

ACTION ITEM 5: IMPROVE YOUR LIGHTING DESIGN

In your home, you likely spend time in the areas that offer the best comfort—and light. And to enhance your experience in those areas and throughout your home, you want to pay particular attention to your lighting design—that is, the strategic placement of natural light and artificial light in your home. The California Energy Commission's Public Interest Energy Research division reports that daylight produces feelings of well-being. It's also associated with increased productivity and reduced absenteeism at schools and in the workplace. The better the natural lighting, the less you'll need to use artificial lighting. Better lighting design is one way to help you save money and feel great. Good natural light is absolutely healthy, money smart, and as long as the sun glows, sustainable.

If your goal is to make the best use of light in your inside zone, you can always call on the help of an interior lighting designer. Ask your agent or friends for a referral. Go online and research lighting options or visit a local store that specializes in lighting. Ideally, what you want is to spend a few minutes talking with a trained lighting designer, an eco-consultant that knows how to select the best artificial light sources to complement the natural light you have.

Remember, you can have the perfect paint on the wall, the perfect furniture on the floor, and the perfect portrait of grandma over the mantel, but if the lighting is wrong, your house will never feel quite like home. Here are some strategies that can accent grandma's complexion as well as illuminate the inside zone of your home.

Green Strategies for Improving Your Lighting Design (Action Item 5)
- Green Strategy I: Embrace Natural Lighting
- Green Strategy II: Choose Smart Artificial Lighting Sources

Green Strategy I: Embrace Natural Lighting

When you're developing your lighting plan for the inside zone of your home, you want to maximize available light entering through your windows or skylights. If you have windows positioned to allow light in, you simply want to open your blinds or curtains and reposition your furniture to avoid blocking the light.

Green Strategy II: Choose Smart Artificial Lighting Sources

With your natural lighting optimized and furniture out of the way, you can now assess your artificial lighting needs. As children, we grew up with inefficient incandescent lightbulbs that produced a lot of heat. Many of us still use these energy hogs. Thankfully, twenty-first-century lighting technology allows for both aesthetic quality and energy efficiency.

One of the best artificial lighting options is to use compact fluorescent lightbulbs (CFLs). These are high quality, high-performance bulbs that last almost forever. When thinking about your home's lighting needs, the key is to replace your old incandescent bulbs—once they burn out—with better technology. Use what you have first and then upgrade to this smarter option.

When it comes to selecting the best CFL for your home, you may first need to experiment to find the right level of brightness. This is easy to do—just make sure that you buy bulbs with the proper lumens (amount of light produced) and wattage (power consumed) for the lamps or light sockets you plan to use them in. Energy Star research suggests keeping your CFL bulbs on for a few minutes—they take time to reach maximum brightness. Look for deals on CFLs at your local home-improvement store.

> *Since 2007, Buckingham Palace has installed 32,000 LED bulbs in the ceiling of its Grand Staircase, as well as LEDs in chandeliers and on the palace's exterior. As a result, lighting up the entire outside of the structure is said to use less electricity than running an electric tea kettle.*
> (Source: "Green Promise Seen in Switch to LED Lighting," *The New York Times*, May 30, 2009)

A final note of caution: Because they contain trace amounts of the toxin mercury, disposal of CFLs is an issue—when they do reach the end of their 10,000-hour life span, these bulbs need to be specially recycled. Many stores that sell CFLs are voluntarily launching recycling programs. Look for one in your area so you can drop off used bulbs in a responsible manner.

Another great artificial lighting alternative to incandescents are light-emitting diode bulbs, or LEDs. You've probably seen them before—they are now very common for holiday and Christmas light decorations. They're also widely available in new car headlights. The beauty of LEDs is in their brightness, safety, and longevity. They provide a nice directional light and none of the dangerous mercury found in CFLs. The temperature and color of the LEDs is measured the same way as CFLs. And while they are more expensive, they actually last much longer than CFLs and are typically much brighter. If you have it in your budget, consider adding LEDs to your mix of artificial lighting sources.

Green Tips: Lighting for Enjoyment and Efficiency

1. Make the most of natural light. From sunrise to sunset, selectively allow sunlight to enter your home to provide free, warm light. Combined with well-designed artificial lighting, natural lighting is a great way to boost efficiency.

2. Meet the new lightbulb in town. Replace your burned-out incandescent lightbulbs with CFLs or LEDs. Simply swapping out the five most commonly used incandescent bulbs in your home can save you $60 to $100 a year.

3. Check out smarter options. Dimmers, daylight sensors, and motion sensors are great devices that automatically turn off unneeded light. And then again, you can always turn off lights manually. There's never a good reason to leave a light on in an empty room.

ACTION ITEM 6: BOOST ENERGY EFFICIENCY

As you've immersed yourself in the pages of this book, it's natural that you may now be considering taking on other action items inside your home to improve its functionality. We know from experience how one item tends to lead to another. And as homeowners, we love the idea of improving the overall performance of our living space. With the next action item, we'd like to encourage you to take stock of some of the things in your inside zone that contribute to your energy consumption. Assessing your energy use requires awareness of how you use energy every day and the ways you may be wasting it. Caring about how much energy you use inside is good for your wallet, and you'll sleep soundly at night knowing you're not wasting energy or money! So where do you begin? How about using the following money-smart strategies to know when you don't need power, how to eliminate phantom power, and how to get the best performance out of your appliances.

Green Strategies for Boosting Energy Efficiency (Action Item 6)
- Green Strategy I: Sometimes You Don't Need Power
- Green Strategy II: Take Control of Your Phantom Load
- Green Strategy III: Make Your Appliances Perform

Green Strategy I: Sometimes You Don't Need Power

It may seem hard to believe, but there are actually times when you don't need energy at all, even to accomplish your to-do list of weekend chores. At these times, being money smart is being able to recognize the opportunities to turn off the power and, instead, rely on Mother Nature. Using drying racks or clotheslines is one great example. Your clothes will last longer and smell better when put out in the sun to dry instead of using the harsh heat of a dryer. And there is no comparison between the amount of money and energy saved when using the great outdoors vs. a clothes dryer.

Another simple way to boost your energy efficiency is to recognize that a room doesn't need to be powered up when you're not in it. Watching a movie in your living room? You don't need to leave the lights on in the kitchen after you make popcorn. Cooking dinner in your kitchen? No need to leave the television on down the hall for Fido the dog. Working out of the office today? No reason to leave your computer buzzing away. Without question, these behavior modifications are easy ways for anyone to save energy and cash.

Green Strategy II: Take Control of Your Phantom Load

Bet you didn't know it, but you're living with a vampire. The silent sucking sound of vampire power is also referred to as our "phantom load." This is the energy wasted when our appliances are plugged into the electric socket and turned off or in standby mode. Your inside zone is home to several phantom power offenders. Typical violators include power adapters like your cell phone charger, TVs, microwave ovens, and computers. All are guilty of draining energy when not actually turned on. This means a whole lot of energy is being used in your home without anyone actually enjoying it, even Fido the dog. And this squandered energy from our electronic devices can account for as much as 10 percent of our home energy use annually. What does this mean for your wallet? Let's say your annual energy bill is $2,200, on average. Then you are spending $220 per year on power that you aren't even aware you're using. What a waste!

Still don't believe it's an issue? Here's a powerful case in point. When it's in standby mode—turned off, but plugged in—a plasma-screen TV might use energy to the tune of $20 per year. It might not seem like much, but if you multiply that number by the number of plasma-screen TVs in circulation, that's millions of dollars in wasted energy. The impact of vampire power on energy consumption is so serious that the California Energy Commission passed a measure in 2009 that would enforce strict television energy-use standards.

Green Tips: Defeat the Menace That Is Phantom Power

1. Plug in and save. You can look for energy savings by plugging your electronic devices into power strips. Just a few power strips strategically placed throughout the inside zone of your home will suffice. Be sure to turn the power strip switch off when your electrical devices are not in use. It can save you money and energy and do a world of good.

2. Set it up right. Group certain devices like your TV or entertainment system (except the DVR!) together on one power strip, and other devices like your computer and a nearby lamp on another.

---

3. Consider energy-monitoring gadgets. From basic electrical outlet monitors to whole house power monitors, the technology available to track your energy use now takes the guesswork out of household energy consumption.

Green Strategy III: Make Your Appliances Perform

Another strategy for making your inside zone more money smart is to make sure your appliances are performing up to par. This means making sure they are running at their optimal level and that you are getting the biggest bang for your buck from each of them. If you've done all you can to get them to perform, they may need to be retired and replaced with newer and better technology.

The key to making sure that your appliances are running their best: Just take care of them. Surprisingly, something as simple as keeping your clothes dryer free from lint can help keep your energy costs more manageable. While using dryer sheets makes your clothes baby soft, they can also make your dryer perform at less than its peak over time, according to Energy Star. So empty your dryer lint tray every time you do a load of wash, and clean the lint filter once a month with an old toothbrush to remove the film left behind by the dryer sheets. Together, these measures can prevent your dryer from chugging away with decreased airflow and can help it work to its best potential to save you money.

Refrigerators and dust are not a good combination when it comes to energy efficiency. So, to keep your refrigerator running at its best, we suggest you also make a habit of consistently cleaning your refrigerator coils. Despite what you might think, the dreaded cleaning of your refrigerator is not a complicated process. Start by pulling the refrigerator out from the wall and unplugging it or turning off its circuit breaker. Find the coils, which are usually tucked behind a removable cover panel, near the bottom of the unit. Once you've taken off the cover, you can use your vacuum or a long-handled brush to clean out the gunk from the coils. That's all it takes. And if you're uncomfortable doing it, ask a professional for help. Your refrigerator's manufacturer might provide guidance as to how frequently this cleaning process is recommended. It may seem like an annoyance, but trust us, cleaning your refrigerator's coils is an easy, money-smart way to cut back your energy usage in the inside zone.

If you regularly upkeep your appliances but still feel like they are money drainers, you should check how old they are. If they're more than a decade old, you're ready for an Energy Star replacement that will save money and energy over time. With every home appliance purchase, there are two costs to consider. First, there is the initial cost of purchase. This is the sticker price of the appliance. Then, there is the operating cost, the amount that it costs you each year to run and maintain the appliance. The operating cost of a newer Energy Star model will be considerably lower than an older, non–energy efficient model. Luckily, these days we have the EnergyGuide label, a bright yellow sticker that is affixed to appliances to help you navigate your shopping trip. The beauty of these labels is that they allow us to look at the amount of energy used by the appliance in a typical year. So, in comparing the labels from one product to the next, we can make a smart buying decision when it comes to purchasing almost any appliance.

If you have the budget to replace one appliance and are not sure which one to start with, focus on the one that contributes the most to your energy bill and the one you bring home the bacon for: the fridge. Many places have recycling programs for old refrigerators that take the hassle out of getting rid of them.

How to Use the EnergyGuide Label

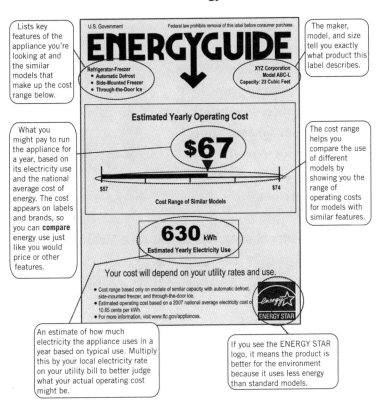

Figure 13 – The EnergyGuide label will tell you everything you've ever wanted to know about an appliance's use of energy and what you'll likely pay to run it year-round. (*Source: U.S. Federal Trade Commission*)

Some even offer you a rebate to replace them. Check with your local municipality to see what's offered in your area.

A SUSTAINABLE INSIDE ZONE

It's now time to take on two more action items in your inside zone—this time with sustainability in mind. Here, we'll focus on easy ways to ensure your home is doing its part to conserve natural resources. Let's continue our Green Your Home adventure in the inside zone by looking at water-efficient appliances and sustainable flooring and finishes.

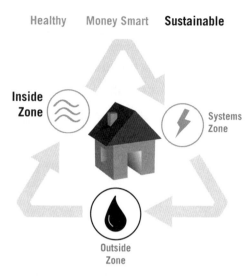

Figure 14 – Sustainability in the inside zone is about water efficiency and interior finishes built to last.

Two Action Items for Making Your Inside Zone More Sustainable

Action Item (7)   Get Water Wise

Action Item (8)   Add Smart, Sustainable Interior Design Features

ACTION ITEM 7: GET WATER WISE

You've probably heard the saying "waste not, want not" many times over the course of your life. And you probably try to do a pretty good job at conserving resources. But there are simple water-wise things that you might not be doing that can take your water conservation capabilities even further. We'll show you how.

Green Strategies for Getting Water Wise in the Inside Zone

- Green Strategy I: Choose Water-Efficient Appliances
- Green Strategy II: Change How You Use Water Indoors

Green Strategy I: Choose Water-Efficient Appliances

Now it's time to talk about water-efficient appliances. The two appliances you want to be mindful of when it comes to efficient water usage are the clothes washer and dishwasher. As always, if possible, Energy Star appliances are the way to go. Ideally, you want to use a front-loading clothes washing unit that takes less water to fill and less energy to run. You also want to make sure you have a full load and use cold water. When it comes to your dishwasher, the rules are similar. Make sure you run it when it's full, vs. only having the dinner plates from last night in it. Some dishwashers have an "economy" or "air dry" cycle, which does not use heat to dry the dishes. If your machine has one of these cycles, use it. And if you have ever wondered about the advantages of hand washing vs. automatic dishwashing, let research done by Energy Star put your mind at ease. When compared to manual dish duty, using an Energy Star dishwasher saves time, money and water every time—each year more than 230 hours of personal time you'd likely need to spend on this chore, $40 on water bills, and almost 5,000 gallons of water! Not only that, the water temperature of an automatic dishwasher is higher than what your delicate hands are capable of handling, which means your dishes will be cleaner after using the appliance as well. Saving money, conserving water and simplifying your chores. Now that's what we call efficient.

Green Strategy II: Change How You Use Water Indoors

The best way to save water is not to waste it. Don't watch your water go down the drain while you're brushing your teeth or cleaning tonight's dinner off your dishes. Turn it off when you aren't using it.

Also, favor showers over baths. Unless you take a twenty-minute Hollywood shower, baths can require more than twice the amount of water as the average shower. Opting for reasonably short showers will save you water and energy and help keep your utility bill low.

ACTION ITEM 8: ADD SMART, SUSTAINABLE INTERIOR DESIGN FEATURES

There are three keys to ensuring an interior design feature qualifies as green. First, it must be made of materials that are less destructive to the planet. Why cut down the Amazon rainforest to extract wood for a patio table when there are beautiful, rapidly renewable alternatives like bamboo available? Second, the sustainable feature should be, well, sustainable. It should be well-constructed, durable and built to last. And third, it must be toxin-free. With these keys in mind, we believe your choices in finishes and flooring can be the biggest and easiest opportunities for adding sustainable features to the inside zone.

Green Strategies for Adding Smart, Sustainable Interior Design Features (Action Item 8)

- Green Strategy I: Choose Sustainable Paint Finishes
- Green Strategy II: Choose Sustainable Flooring

Green Strategy I: Choose Sustainable Paint Finishes

When it comes to the appearance of your inside zone, the finishes you choose are crucial. Finishes are the outer layers that give your home its definitive look. And one of the most important finishes you can choose in your home is your paint. There are two pieces to think about when it comes to purchasing paint: makeup and aesthetics. Because you'll be breathing in the rooms you paint in your inside zone, you need to know what's in the paint you're using. That is, what the paint is made of. When it comes to aesthetics, it's important to look into the paint's quality—whether it will crack easily and if applying multiple coats is necessary. And, of course, you'll want to explore the collection of colors that are available.

Paint technology has come such a long way since the days of using lead as an ingredient. Nowadays all paints you choose will be lead-free. But paint is still paint, and most paint contains some potentially harmful substances. If you remember from earlier in this chapter, the VOCs are the volatile organic compounds put into products to get them to perform (stick to walls, in this case). VOCs in paint are dangerous to breathe and can take years to fully off-gas. You'll want to look for low- or no-VOC varieties available from your local home improvement or hardware store. Or if you have the budget and extreme sensitivities, there are even natural paint products derived from milk or plants like soy. No matter which brand you choose, you'll want to opt for water-based paints. There are many great cost-competitive brands, of which many are certified green by third-party organizations like Green Seal. (A list of Green Seal-certified products can be found at www.greenseal.org.) These paints come in an array of amazing colors. So if you have an ambitious palette—there's likely a safer option available for you in both latex and acrylic.

When it comes to doing the actual painting of your walls, a good rule of thumb is to make sure you ventilate like crazy. You want fresh air and you want a steady supply of it. The gases from even low-VOC paints will remain present for a long time. If you're uncomfortable with the painting part, you can always ask your real estate agent for a few referrals to get the job done.

Green Strategy II: Choose Sustainable Flooring

With your green-friendly paint on the walls, it's now time to turn to the many sustainable flooring options at your disposal. Trust us, there are many! Some of the more common products include stained or polished concrete, hardwood, carpet, bamboo, cork, tile and, believe it or not, sustainable laminate options. Any of these products might make a good match for your decorating needs. You will need to do research to make the best informed decision. You'll start by weighing the options and thinking about your comfort (do you want a hard, cold floor or a warm, soft floor), your stylistic preferences (beautiful hardwoods or quirky cork), and on how green you actually want to go.

Your decision will also depend on what's available and at what cost. Flooring can be a significant expense, so what you buy must make sense for your budget. It's also important to include the cost of labor for installing specialized flooring. Ask your agent for the names of a few contractors. No matter what you decide, keep in mind that deep green flooring meets the same criteria as sustainable finishes: It should be eco-friendly, durable, and not dangerous to your health. Let's take a look at the pros and cons of some sustainable flooring options.

ANALYZING FLOORING CHOICES

FLOORING	PROS	CONS	IMPORTANT CONSIDERATIONS
Stained or Polished Concrete	• Affordable, especially when it's your foundation pulling double duty • As durable as it gets • Can be paired with a radiant floor-heating system	• Concrete is extremely resource intensive • Can be chilly on bare feet	• Because of the high environmental impact of producing and shipping concrete, choose it when you intend it to last a lifetime • Look for a high percentage of fly ash, a recycled by-product • Seal and stain it with low-emission products
Hardwood	• Moderate cost • Durable • Can refinish • Great for adaptive reuse	• If it's not certified, may contribute to deforestation	• Use reclaimed or Forest Stewardship Council (FSC)-certified wood products *continued*

FLOORING	PROS	CONS	IMPORTANT CONSIDERATIONS
Carpet	• Cheap • Nice to walk on in bare feet	• Wears out quickly and difficult to recycle • Harbors dust and pollutants and requires deep cleaning • Most brands made of petrochemicals • Many contain high toxin levels and PVCs	• Consider carpet tiles, which allow replacement of worn spots only • Look for recycled content • Look for natural content such as wool, hemp, or jute • Look for Scientific Certification System or Green Label Plus certification
Bamboo	• Moderate cost • A rapidly renewable grass • Fairly durable	• May contain toxic sealants or finishes • Grown in Asia – high carbon footprint	• Look for low-VOC products
Cork	• Rapidly renewable • Soft on the feet and provides a spring • A good insulator to keep floors on the warm side	• May not be durable in wet or very humid areas • Mainly grown in Europe – high carbon footprint	• Look for low-VOC products

continued

ANALYZING FLOORING CHOICES (CONTINUED)

FLOORING	PROS	CONS	IMPORTANT CONSIDERATIONS
Tile	• Durable • Locally produced options are increasingly available • Repairable (by replacing individual tiles)	• Energy-intensive to produce • Grout can stain	• Look for recycled glass or ceramic content • Use formaldehyde-free, low-VOC backing, sealants, and grout
Laminates	• Cheap	• Often not durable • Often contain toxins	• Choose recycled, cork, or bamboo versions • Choose snap-together brands to minimize adhesives • Find the low-VOC options to ensure minimal pollutant emission

Figure 15

It's no surprise that there is no perfect product for your home. There are benefits and drawbacks to each of the options. Some are greener than others and some cost more than others. You'll want to consider the pros and cons before you settle on the best choice for your home.

A HEALTHY INSIDE ZONE IS A FEW ACTION ITEMS AWAY

First, we walked you through four green improvement action items and related strategies for boosting the health of your inside zone. Then, we provided additional action items that can make your inside zone more money smart and sustainable. If done right and with the right team of experts, each of these will help improve your air quality, lighting comfort, energy usage, and water consumption. Now it's up to you to be proactive and select the action items that are most appropriate for your own inside zone. So build your list and rest assured that each of these items will take you one step closer to your goal of achieving a truly healthy inside zone. Next, we'll continue step 3 of our process by zeroing in on being money smart in the systems zone through a focus on energy.

CHAPTER 4:
THE SYSTEMS ZONE

The cheapest energy is the energy you don't use in the first place.

SHERYL CROW, SINGER/SONGWRITER

THE BONDS' STORY: RICKETY FARMHOUSE TO HIGH-PERFORMANCE HOME

In the beginning, home was whatever kept you dry and warm. A cave, a hut, a lean-to—anything to keep the rain and cold out. We've since gotten better at adapting these basic shelters into homes that perform in a wide range of climates and conditions. For example, in the Southwest portion of North America, people discovered that thick adobe walls keep you cool under the desert sun and warm at night. They also learned to build high ceilings and porches to catch every breeze possible, while their northern neighbors were building saltbox cottages with windowless backs for added protection against the cold winds. Now in the twenty-first century, we've reached a new level: homes that function like money-smart machines to allow maximum control over our energy and water use at minimum cost.

Design-builder Ed Bond lives in a home that literally embodies this march of progress. He bought his 1842 Massachusetts farmhouse in 1974. He and his wife Ellen chose the house because it was situated on a pristine acre and a half with a brook full of trout, and it was what they could afford for $12,000. They thought they'd stay a few years, fix it up, and move on. Fixing it up turned out to be no small proposition, however. The home still had its nineteenth-century insulation system, which is to say, it had four walls and a roof. The kitchen was directly over a drafty dirt-floored crawlspace, and on the second floor, the outside walls of the home enjoyed the combined protection of some tacked-up newspaper and some peeling flowered wallpaper. As a result, most of the heat generated by their electric system leaked straight out into the frigid Berkshires air. So they kept it off most of the time and relied instead on an old cast-iron woodstove. Even so, their heating bills were $800 a year (almost $3,300 in today's inflation-adjusted dollars) and their house was *still* 45 degrees most winter mornings! Ed and Ellen suffered through that first winter, and by spring, they were winterizing their home with a purpose.

Over the next three decades, Ed's mission continued to be improving the systems zone of their home—the heating, cooling, ventilation, electrical, and plumbing considerations. He recognized the importance of tightening the building envelope, so he added an inch of foam to the outside of the home before adding new siding, making sure every crack and cranny was tightly sealed in the process. He then sprayed foam insulation around the perimeter of the home and in the crawlspace to keep cold basement air from leaking upstairs and added brand-new insulation inside the walls. Recognizing that improving the home's systems zone required greening his home from the *inside* out, he took the old bottle-glass out of the weathered wood windows and replaced it with efficient double panes.

As the years went by, Ed and Ellen kept going. In the 1980s, they continued to improve their systems by retrofitting the roof structure to accommodate extra-thick insulation. Ed bought pleated shades for all the windows to keep heat in at night. He used his background in corporate electronics to design a solar hot-water system and equipped the south-facing porch to capture and store the natural heat from the sun.

"It became a complete lifestyle, the process of trying to turn this house from a very dilapidated situation with very little money and hard work," says Ed. "Every year was a new project."

In 2009, he finished a new skylight in the master bathroom so Ellen could grow plants there and he added a metal roof. Next stop: new solar panels. And the house that Ed thought he'd sell to someone else in a few years has become his forever home. "I thought we'd stay for five years, and thirty-five years later, we're still here."

IN THE SYSTEMS ZONE: MONEY SMART IS YOUR 20 PERCENT

Earlier in this book, we talked about how being money smart is an important driver in many people's decisions to go green. And when we talk about saving money through making green home improvements, most of the discussion is about energy. The drawback to energy is its cost, both in terms of money and natural resources. And while the price of energy fluctuates, we know it's not likely to get much cheaper anytime soon. So it pays to be money smart about the way we use energy in our homes. We can accomplish this by maximizing our energy efficiency and financial savings over the long haul and minimizing the burning of fossil fuels in the process. It's good for our wallets and our planet.

The key to a money-smart systems zone is an efficient, high-performance home environment. This means honing in on how you use energy to heat, cool, and ventilate every day. If you remember the 80/20 Principle from chapter 1, your dedicated focus on being money smart, your 20 percent in this case, will deliver 80 percent of your results: the green improvements you will realize. Finding ways to conserve energy through improvements we suggest in this chapter will pay dividends over time. And you don't have to be an expert when it comes to your home's systems either. Your team of professionals will be there to help when you need it. You just need to be aware of and focus on efficiency when you are looking at the various pieces of the systems in your home. As a bonus, there are also ways to boost home health and save water. We'll cover a few action items to help you do just that in the systems zone.

PROJECT 2: MASTER LIST FOR THE SYSTEMS ZONE

PRIORITY	ACTION ITEMS
Money Smart	1. Understand How You Use Energy • *Take a Hard Look at Your Utility Bill* • *Establish a Baseline with an Energy Audit* 2. Pay Yourself Back with Easy Energy Updates • *Install a Digital Thermostat* • *Light Your Way to Savings* 3. Tighten the Building Envelope • *Seal the Gaps* • *Patch Your Ducts* • *Beef Up Your Insulation* • *Improve Your Windows' Performance* *continued*

PRIORITY	ACTION ITEMS (CONTINUED)

Energy	4. Maintain Your Mechanical Heating and Cooling System
	   • *Stay Warm*
	   • *Keep Cool*
	
	5. Work with Nature
	   • *Take Advantage of Natural Heating Techniques*
	   • *Incorporate Natural Cooling Methods*

Healthy	6. Optimize Your Ventilation System
	   • *Change Your System's Air Filter*
	   • *Consider a Whole-House Ventilation System*

Sustainability	7. Upgrade the Water-Wise Way
	   • *Understand Your Water Bill*
	   • *Install Low-Flow Showerheads and Faucet Aerators*
	   • *Transform Your Toilet*
	   • *Improve Your Hot-Water Heater*

Figure 16

CONTINUING STEP 3: BUILD YOUR GREEN PROJECT LIST IN THE SYSTEMS ZONE

Although improvements to the systems zone may feel less enticing or less exciting than visible ones in the inside zone, they are still a key component of a greener home.

"It is critical to visualize the home as a system and make sure the entire project is as efficient and healthy as possible before worrying about selecting materials that are more sustainable," says Carl Seville, a green building consultant in Atlanta, Georgia. "If you put good materials on an otherwise poorly performing house, you have essentially put lipstick on a pig. It is still a pig."

So with that in mind, let's pick up where we left off in the inside zone and continue working on step 3 of the Green Your Home process in the systems zone. In this chapter, we'll help you green your home from the inside out—just like Ed and Ellen Bond did by focusing on their systems zone throughout their farmhouse renovation. It involves a number of action items that you and your team can undertake over the long term. You'll learn how to find out if your home is operating at its peak performance level. And we'll show you how to make the changes your home needs to be as efficient as possible. Are you ready? Then let's dive into your money-smart systems zone.

A MONEY-SMART SYSTEMS ZONE

Now, let's tackle the main priority of the systems zone—being money smart. We've assembled our list of five money-smart projects and encourage you to begin with the one that's easiest for you. The

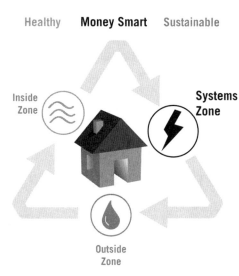

Figure 17 – Energy efficiency is one of the keys to a money-smart systems zone.

first action items are the easiest to take on, the lowest hanging fruit that will help you attain your goals. However, each one of these five can help you reduce your energy footprint—your overall energy consumption—and lower your energy bill.

Five Action Items for Making Your Systems Zone More Money Smart

Action Item (1)   Understand how you use energy.

Action Item (2)   Pay yourself back with easy energy updates.

Action Item (3)   Tighten the building envelope.

Action Item (4)   Maintain your mechanical heating and cooling system.

Action Item (5)   Work with nature.

ACTION ITEM 1: UNDERSTAND HOW YOU USE ENERGY

How is your home performing in terms of energy usage? Do you keep an eye on your monthly energy bill? Are you aware of how much your household spends on energy at different times of the year? How much energy does your household actually consume in a year? Once you know the answers to these questions, you can then ask yourself and your team of experts if you're doing as much as you can to keep your systems as energy efficient as possible.

Green Strategies for Understanding How You Use Energy (Action Item 1)

- Green Strategy I: Take a Hard Look at Your Utility Bill
- Green Strategy II: Establish a Baseline with an Energy Audit

Green Strategy I: Take a Hard Look at Your Utility Bill

Now's the time to take out those energy bills or contact your local utility provider and request at least two years' worth of documentation. According to the U.S. Energy Information Administration, the average cost of electricity for residential households in the United States in 2009 was close to 11¢ per kilowatt-hour (kWh). The average annual energy bill in 2009 was $2,200. Natural Resources Canada reports that the cost per kWh is 7.5¢, and the average annual energy bill is $2,318 (2008 statistics). Do you know how much your energy bill totaled in the last year?

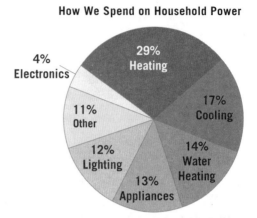

How We Spend on Household Power

Figure 18 – Annual energy bill for a typical single family home is approximately $2,200.
(Source: Typical House memo. Lawrence Berkley National Laboratory, 2009)

The graphic "How We Spend on Household Power" indicates where our money typically goes to power our homes.

Here's a simple exercise you've probably never considered. It will help you understand how you use energy. Count the number of lightbulbs inside your home. More than likely, you have no idea how many lights you have, but you still use many of them every day. How many of these bulbs are energy-hog incandescents? How many are cost-saving CFLs? As we told you in the last chapter, small steps like changing just five incandescent bulbs to CFLs can take you a long way toward saving energy and being more money smart. And that's just the beginning. Once you make the change, you'll see how improvements are reflected in a lower energy bill. Keep in mind that the best way to compare your bills is through a year-over-year analysis, which will show you your usage patterns and may uncover any unusual discrepancies. Once you've completed your review, you're ready for the next step: an energy audit.

Green Strategy II: Establish a Baseline with an Energy Audit

For a six-year-old home, Ken Williams' residence in Madison, Wisconsin, did a poor job of delivering comfort. No matter how much he ran the air conditioner in the muggy summers, the home always stayed slightly humid and warm. In the winter, it was always chilly. He would light a fire in the fireplace, thinking the crackling blaze would make things cozier. Instead, it got colder! The whole thing was a mystery to Ken. After all, it was a home built with energy efficiency in mind. The proverbial lightbulb (compact fluorescent, of course) went on for Ken when he heard about home-performance evaluators or energy raters—eco-consultants trained to ferret out the source of drafts, weird smells, and other signs of an underperforming home system. As a real estate agent and EcoBroker, Ken's interest was both personal and professional. He wanted to know from firsthand experience whether the evaluation was worth the $250 cost.

The performance evaluator showed up at the door with a van full of high-tech equipment, like a Ghostbuster minus the ectoplasm—a Leakbuster, so to speak. For three hours, his equipment whirred and buzzed and flashed. The inspector closed all the doors and windows to set up a blower door test. He used a fan that sucked the air out of the house, which created a low-pressure zone inside the house that made it easy to identify sources of leakage. In Ken's case, the test revealed strong drafts flowing in through a bad seal around a sliding glass door. The inspector also had an infrared camera that showed the temperature of objects in different colors—the darker the color, the warmer the object.

That's how the evaluator quickly solved the mystery of how the fireplace was making Ken's family colder. When he trained the camera on two recessed light fixtures in the ceiling of the living room, right in front of the fireplace, the fixtures were an entirely different color from the rest of the ceiling. "It turns out those two fixtures were essentially holes in my ceiling, and whenever I used the fireplace, the holes were sucking cold air from the outside right into the living room," says Ken. As popular as they are, recessed can lights will often be near the top of most lists of "don'ts" when it comes to energy efficiency. So it pays to invoke the help of a lighting specialist when installing these fixtures in your home to ensure they are properly sealed and insulated.

Home-performance evaluators not only point out problems, they can also direct you to contractors who can fix the problem and suggest federal or local programs that can help pay for upgrades. In fact, a performance evaluation is often a required first step if you're going to apply for rebate programs, and in some places the government even pays for them.

In the United States, visit energysavers.gov. In Canada, visit the Office of Energy Efficiency at oee.nrcan.gc.ca/English/ to learn about the programs the government offers to help Canadians become more energy efficient.

The inspector found something even more disturbing. The builder of the home had forgotten to insulate the ceiling, meaning that a huge chunk of Ken's heat and air conditioning was simply dissipating into the atmosphere rather than staying inside the home where it could keep him comfortable. "The calculation indicated that the lack of insulation in that 500-square-foot area was costing us at least $300 annually in increased energy costs," says Ken. He immediately contacted an insulation contractor to fix the issue. He also knew from then on what he'd tell clients who asked whether a performance evaluation is worth it: *"Absolutely!"*

Whether you've got rebates and incentives in mind, we always recommend a performance evaluation to help you pinpoint problems and know exactly what you're working with. In fact, once you decide to take on many of the action items and strategies we suggest in this book, we strongly encourage you to make sure a home energy audit is at the top of your list. You'll get an education and practical direction about problem areas in your home's systems zone.

ACTION ITEM 2: PAY YOURSELF BACK WITH EASY ENERGY UPDATES

You now have a better understanding of how you use energy. Your bills tell the story. You've added an energy audit to your soon-to-do list to pinpoint areas for improvement. So now we'd like you to take stock of two other components in the systems zone of your home that contribute to your energy consumption: your thermostat and efficiency enhancements to your artificial lighting. In our opinion, you can't address the systems zone of the home and your energy footprint without looking at the smaller pieces that affect them. So let's take a look at these small, but important energy-influencers in your systems zone.

Green Strategies to Pay Yourself Back with Easy Energy Updates (Action Item 2)

- Green Strategy I: Install a Digital Thermostat
- Green Strategy II: Light Your Way to Savings

Green Strategy I: Install a Digital Thermostat

The human body operates at close to 98.6 degrees whether it's freezing cold or fiery hot outside. We call this homeostasis, a natural balancing act we support by bundling up when it's cold and sweating when it's hot. Inside our homes, we prefer a temperature that's fairly comfortable and predictable as well. We use energy to find an optimal balance between heating and cooling. Surprisingly, we use so much energy for setting the right temperature that it accounts for close to 50 percent of our utility expenses each year. So again, using the $2,200 average annual utility bill example, you'll likely spend $1,100 a year on heating and cooling!

According to the U.S. Department of Energy, you can save somewhere in the neighborhood of 10 percent on your annual energy bill by simply turning your thermostat back 10 to 15 percent for eight hours.

A great way to conserve your energy consumption and save money without actively thinking about it all the time is to install a digital thermostat. Digital thermostats can be programmed to heat and cool your home at different temperatures depending upon the time of day or day of the week. If you prefer, you can even buy one that's conveniently preprogrammed, such as an Energy Star model that comes out of the package with automatic settings in place.

With a digital thermostat, you enable the heating and cooling systems of your home to work more efficiently when you're at home and when you're away. All you need to do is choose a great model for about $50, install it, or call on an electrician or HVAC professional for help and select the setting that works best for your household.

Green Tips: Using Your Digital Thermostat to Drive Down Costs

1. Don't ignore the instructions. Read the instruction manual to familiarize yourself with the programmable or preprogrammed temperature-setting options on your unit.

2. Placement matters. The location of your thermostat determines the operating efficiency of your heating and cooling system. Keep direct sunlight, lamps, and other heat-producing appliances away from your unit. If you need to reposition your thermostat, you should call in an HVAC professional.

3. Base it on your routine. Program the thermostat according to your household's schedule, or choose preprogrammed settings that maintain a temperature for when you're at home for long periods and away from home for several hours at a time, as well as when you're asleep at night.

4. Keep it running. Be sure to check the batteries for your unit and replace them once a year. We recommend replacing your batteries for your smoke detectors and thermostat at the same time. If you're lucky, your thermostat unit might even remind you when it's ready for a new battery.

Green Strategy II: Light Your Way to Savings

Like your thermostat, did you know that lighting actually contributes to about 10 percent of overall energy use? With the same average energy bill figure of $2,200, your lighting accounts for $220 of your bill each year. If you're like us and hate the idea of wasting money, then you should look at this additional strategy for saving money in your systems zone through smarter lighting options. If you recall from chapter 3, we shared strategies for improving your lighting in the inside zone. Hopefully, you've taken a good look at your lighting and replaced some of your incandescent bulbs with CFLs. Now you can go a step further by using Energy Star *lighting fixtures* on your walls and ceilings, for things like your bathroom vanities, wall sconces, chandeliers and ceiling lights. These Energy Star fixtures differ from traditional lighting fixtures in that most require specialized pin-based CFL bulbs that must last 10,000 hours (compared to the already impressive minimum of 6,000 hours that a typical CFL bulb lasts). If you're looking to update your lighting fixtures, consider installing an Energy Star product. There are many options available and these can be found at a variety of retailers. With a combination of Energy Star fixtures and pin-based CFL bulbs, you can save even more money.

ACTION ITEM 3: TIGHTEN THE BUILDING ENVELOPE

With your energy audit complete and ways to keep your home's energy consumption in check, the next step is to make sure all the nooks and crannies of your home are properly sealed. This is a big action item. It can be hard to take tiny leaks seriously, especially when there are more fun projects to consider, like incorporating recycled glass tiles into your backsplash. However, all of your home's little leaks can add up to one big problem and compromise your ability to be money smart in your home.

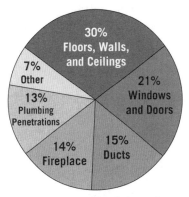

Figure 19 – Here's a breakdown of energy leaks in a typical home.

Unless you live in a moderate climate such as Los Angeles, California, where you rarely heat or cool your home and can spend most of the time with the windows open, tightening your building envelope—the technical term for the floors, walls, ceilings, and other structural elements that separate the inside from the outside—is one of the best steps you can take toward a greener home. Tightening up a home has four strategies.

Green Strategies for Tightening the Building Envelope (Action Item 3)

- Green Strategy I: Seal the Gaps
- Green Strategy II: Patch Your Ducts
- Green Strategy III: Beef Up Your Insulation
- Green Strategy IV: Improve Your Windows' Performance

Green Tip: The Anatomy of a Draft

Leaks, drafts, and poor air quality are all related to the same phenomenon: pressure differences between air of different temperatures. We know it may be tempting, but don't tune out now. This is the science behind one of the invisible, but essential, keys to an energy-efficient home. Imagine two rooms next to each other: one is very cold and the other very warm. Donna Do-It-Yourselfer is standing in the cold room, shivering and fantasizing about beaches in Miami, Florida. She then goes over to the warm room. She notices the difference, and suddenly she's thinking about a ski trip to Whistler, British Columbia. What she doesn't notice, however, is that the cold room is actually at a *higher pressure* than the warm room.

Now, imagine that Donna has whipped out the handsome yellow drill she just bought in preparation for her green improvement projects. She turns it on and *vrooom*! She drills a big hole in the wall between the two rooms. Immediately, the high-pressure cold air starts flowing into the warm room in an attempt to equalize the temperature and pressure differences between the two. Voila! Donna has created a wind—a draft—between the two rooms.

You don't need a drill to experience this phenomenon, because, unless you've moved into some kind of super-deluxe, space-age, high-efficiency bubble, you've already got tiny holes in the shell of your building. In the summer, the high-pressure conditioned air pushes out of these holes into the warmer air outside. In the winter, the cold December air literally pushes itself into your home through any tiny crack you've left unsealed. The leaks may not be perceptible, but they add up. The U.S. Department of Energy reports that air leaks in most homes equate to opening a window and leaving it open year-round!

Green Strategy I: Seal the Gaps

Even the thickest insulation won't be able to perform if it's fighting a draft, so sealing gaps in the building envelope is priority one on the road to green. A home is a big place though. So, where should you aim the caulk gun first?

If you think the attic, you're correct! Heat rises, so holes in the attic are particularly good at sucking heated air (for which you're paying) into the atmosphere. Plugging up the leaks amounts to nothing more than getting up there with a caulk gun and firing away at the gaps. Caulk is a sealant compound that comes in many forms, commonly as silicone and polyurethane. It can be applied in a variety of ways, including through the use of a cartridge and gun, squeeze tube, and spray. Once you're a master of the caulk gun, you can use your gap-sealing skills in the seams and outlets of any conditioned space. This should be followed by precision application of strategic weather-stripping around your doors and windows. While we know that each of us is perfectly capable of crawling around, wielding a caulk gun, and chewing bubble gum all at the same time without risking life and limb, we also realize that cobwebs are not everyone's thing. The faint-of-heart and short-on-time homeowners out there can instead hire a contractor who specializes in home-sealing. Your home-performance evaluator or real estate agent can point you to a good contractor.

Green Tips: Sealing Your Home's Gaps for Optimal Efficiency

1. Know where to look. First and foremost, you need to establish a baseline in order to know where to start. Let us remind you, it's well worth it to get a professional energy audit done of your home. A blower door test precisely identifies the sources of leakage in your home. But, if you prefer, you can simply walk around your home on a cold day, holding your hands over windows, doors, outlets, and seams to feel for drafts.

2. Caulking made easy. To ensure caulking success, make sure that the desired area is clean, dry, and free of old caulk. Keep the caulk gun at a 45-degree angle to penetrate cracks and caulk in one continuous motion. Apply caulk generously to ensure it completely fills any gaps. And keep a putty knife handy, just in case, to smooth out any caulk bumps or wrinkles.

3. In the attic. Caulk around any obvious gaps in the shell of the building. Pay special attention to anywhere plumbing or wiring pokes through the ceiling or walls. Applying spray foam insulation to the underside of the roof acts as both a sealant and insulator.

4. In your inside zone. Caulk around windows, doors and baseboards. Caulk is meant to be permanent, so remember not to use it on anything that has to move. Instead, apply weather-stripping to the parts of your windows and doors that need to move, such as door sweeps or strips of foam between double-hung windows. Add insulated switch plates to your electrical outlets.

5. In your outside zone. Repeat the caulk job you just did around the inside windows and doors on the outside of your home. If you don't have modern, insulated windows, make sure that storm windows are present, accounted for, and in good shape. If you're re-siding your home, look into house-wrapping or exterior insulation.

Green Strategy II: Patch Your Ducts

Boulder, Colorado-based Nate Burger of Eco Handyman received a call from a client who wanted to insulate and seal her home. She told Nate he should pay particular attention to one room on the north side of her home, where it was always cold. He wriggled into the crawlspace to check things out and reached a diagnosis almost immediately. "The entire duct for that room was disconnected from the furnace because the contractor had just taped it on instead of using screws," he says. "No wonder she was cold."

Near-invisible gaps in your envelope are bad. The gaps that many people, like Nate's client, have in their ductwork are just plain silly. Home inspectors say it's a common sight: a disconnected duct lying on the floor of the attic like an octopus with a broken tentacle, blowing hot or cold air into completely uninhabited space. "There are a lot of people spending their hard-earned money air conditioning their attics," says Alabama home inspector Joe Cooper.

So what do ducts have to do with being money smart? A lot! Think of ducts as the veins and arteries of your home. They carry conditioned air from your heating and cooling units and draw fresh air from your return. Like a good blood vessel in your body, they operate best when they are well-sealed, saving you money and requiring less energy to keep your home heated or cooled.

While repairing your ducts is by far easier than performing vascular surgery, you may still need to reach out to a ductwork specialist for help. If you go it alone, you'll want to apply water-based mastic (an adhesive sealant) to all the seams and joints of your ducts to seal any openings. If you discover huge gashes, you can use fiberglass tape and mastic. If you hire a specialist for the job, make sure they do a pressure test. And you might even consider getting your ducts in a row; that is, getting them cleaned at the same time. Like anything else, ducts can get dusty and moldy, and scrubbing them out on occasion can't hurt the quality of your air.

Green Strategy III: Beef Up Your Insulation

Many older homes lack insulation to begin with—remember Ed and Ellen Bond? Before their home improvements, they were protected from the elements by nothing but wallpaper. In other attics, what was once fluffy and pink insulation has grown dingy, flat and unable to perform due to moisture, settling, and plain old age. That's why it's hard to find anyone who doesn't recommend re-insulating as a top priority: It's relatively painless and it pays you back over time.

What's the best place to begin your journey to well-insulated comfort? It shouldn't come as much of a surprise that the same place you first aimed your caulk gun—the attic—should also be the first recipient of new insulation.

Thermal resistance value or R-value is common terminology used to describe insulation products. An R-value measures how well a material or product resists heat flow. Typically, you'll see a product's R-value expressed as "R-" and the number that corresponds to its insulating value. A product with a higher R-value ensures better insulation in your home.

If you live in a hot climate like Tucson, Arizona, we suggest you also add a reflective or radiant barrier to your attic. Technically, they're not considered insulation. Instead, these barriers consist of thin foil layers that reflect heat away from your conditioned space. They can keep your attic up to 30 degrees cooler on a very hot day, which significantly boosts the operations of a home's overall system at a minimal cost.

After the attic, the basement should be next on your list. Insulating the basement has a number of advantages. If your basement is unfinished, a barrier on the underside of your first floor will keep cold, damp, unpleasant air from entering your living space upstairs. In cold climates, you may want to consider actual insulation; in warm, humid climates, a moisture or vapor barrier should do the trick. We don't recommend insulating the walls unless you're already tearing the home apart anyway; it's just too much hassle for not enough value. If you do a gut remodel, however, go ahead and pay extra to raise the R-value of the wall insulation to at least R-18 (or up to R-28 if you're in a particularly cold climate).

Depending upon which type of insulation product you select, insulating your home can be either a fairly low-cost DIY project or a more expensive investment that requires the help of an expert. There are many online resources that provide great instructions for installing insulation if you decide to go it alone, like an online guide we found at EnergyStar.gov. Just be sure to wear protective gear like a facemask, goggles, and gloves for any insulating work you do.

While it's possible to select and safely install insulation yourself, we think it's best to work with a professional who knows all the tricks to ensure the highest long-term performance. "Over 90 percent of insulation I've seen has been incorrectly installed," says Scott Blunk, a green builder in Sacramento, California. "The impression people have is that it's very easy to install. But if there are wires or pipes in the wall, you have to make sure you sandwich insulation around them from both sides or you will get air movement in the walls. You need the insulation to stay fluffy and fill the space. It takes skill to do it right."

Green Tip: Insulate It Right

When you're shopping for insulation, keep two main concerns top of mind: 1) how well it performs and 2) how safe it is. Performance is measured in R-value. Like we mentioned, the higher the R-value, the cozier you'll be. Safety is a measure of how toxic the insulating material may be. Keep these terms in mind as we cover some of the common choices available to you.

Rolled or batted insulation is the fluffy material that looks like giant rolls of cotton candy. It's usually made of fiberglass and generally contains at least 20 percent recycled glass. The tiny fibers of glass that make up the rolls bear a structural resemblance to asbestos and have been declared a possible carcinogen. So it's not exactly safe and you always should wear protective gear when installing it. However, some fiberglass manufacturers have responded with sealed products in an attempt to keep the glass fibers out of the attic and out of your lungs.

Rolled insulation has to be cut into place, which means proper installation can be especially tricky depending upon your attic's layout. Rolled insulation of recycled cotton may be available in your market, although concerns have been raised about its fire resistance. Rolled or batted insulation offers a range of R-values and is one of the more affordable options.

Loose-fill/blown-in insulation usually consists of either fiberglass or cellulose, which is made from recycled newspapers. The beauty of blown-in insulation is that it allows you to achieve a continuous, gap-free layer with more complete coverage than the batted or rolled products. However, it is often treated with fire-retardant chemicals that may raise health concerns.

Because it does not need to be cut into place, it can be easier to install. However, to install this type of insulation, you'll need to rent a machine that actually blows in the material. You can find a rental at a home-improvement store. And while renting a machine may feel like a little more of a hassle, stores often offer discount deals on the rental. It too is ideal for the attic and offers R-values on par or better than the rolled or batted type.

Spray-in is a chemical foam, such as polyurethane or polyisocyanurate, that hardens in place. Unlike other kinds of insulation, spray foam does stop leaks, so if you're using foam you can skip the caulk gun. However, the foaming agent is often a hydrochloroflourocarbon (HCFC), which damages the ozone layer and is a greenhouse gas. Because it performs so well, many home-improvement specialists prefer it on the logic that its long-term savings outweigh the installation concerns. By far it offers the highest R-values, and it works well for attics and ceilings.

Green Strategy IV: Improve Your Windows' Performance

Windows are nothing more than holes in your walls. This makes them remarkably effective at letting light into your home; however, it also makes them remarkably effective at letting heat out. In colder seasons, storm windows can reduce the heat lost through single-paned windows by 25 percent to 50 percent, according to EnergyHog.org. You want windows to have two features: insulation and coatings. Insulation is achieved through multiple layers. Modern windows are not panes of glass as much as they are sandwiches—double or triple panes of glass with argon or krypton gas between them. Coatings block certain wavelengths of sunlight to either keep heat indoors in cold climates, or keep it outside in warmer climates. Low-emittance coatings on the surfaces of windows, also called "low-e," are thin, transparent oxide layers that reflect specific wavelengths of sunlight. The only thing you need to know about low-e windows is that they help control the amount of heat that enters your home. Window technology is constantly evolving and can go a long way to helping you save money on your heating and cooling costs.

With all the great window technology available, you may feel tempted to dash to the home-improvement store to get started on your window-improvement project immediately. Freeze it right there! Windows are an area where it's especially important to weigh the payback time, which can be considerable, especially if you're not planning on staying in your home for at least several years. Of course, federal and state rebates and incentives do help, and you should take full advantage of them when they're available. If you do decide to opt for new high-tech windows, the best time to install them is when you are building an addition, or when your old windows are broken and need to be replaced anyway. It's worth noting that home buyers appreciate new windows, so it can also create a competitive advantage for you when it comes time to sell your home.

In the meantime, you can coax the highest performance out of your existing windows with effective but timeless money-smart techniques. Heavy drapes that you can close at night do a great job keeping heat in. Blinds can keep the direct sun out. One type of effective window treatment is the cellular blind, which helps maintain a stable temperature by providing an extra barrier for your windows, like a blanket, to keep the cold out and the heat in. Lastly, we suggest making sure your storm windows are all present and functional. This is an old-school but effective way to insulate your panes.

So, you now have a trove of wisdom on how to make your building envelope work more effectively. Next, we'll give you some more money-smart advice on how to keep up the mechanical heating and cooling systems of your home. Modern windows are designed to perform, so it's important to choose models that perform best for your home. Choose right by studying the National Fenestration Rating Council (NFRC) label. It's like a nutritional label for windows that lets you compare different products for how well they insulate and what their low-e coatings are engineered to accomplish.

Window insulation is measured with a U-value and typically falls in a range of 0.2 to 1.20. The lower the U-value, the better the window will insulate. So if you live in a cold climate, look for a U-value of 0.35 or less.

The NFRC label also shows the Solar Heat Gain Coefficient (SHGC), which measures on a scale from 0 to 1 how much heat can pass through the window. In warmer climates, you will want to stop as much heat from coming into your home as possible, so look for an SHGC lower than 0.4 (which means less than 40 percent of the sun's heat will enter the room). If you live in a cold climate with mild summers, get windows with a higher SHGC to allow the lower winter sun to heat your home.

Lastly, a NFRC label shows the Visible Transmittance (VT), which indicates how much light will pass through the window. It is measured like SHGC: a window with a VT of 0.6 will allow 60 percent of the light to enter the house and will appear completely clear. Windows with a VT of less than 0.5 will darken the view and should only be

Figure 20 – Most energy-efficient modern windows have National Fenestration Rating Council labels, which show how well they insulate and how much heat and light can pass through the pane.

used in rooms with excessive sunlight and heat. If you're making the significant investment of replacing your windows, it's worth talking to a home-performance expert to determine the right mix of heat and light for your climate, orientation, and home layout.

ACTION ITEM 4: MAINTAIN YOUR MECHANICAL SYSTEMS

Heating and cooling accounts for your greatest energy expenses, according to Energy Star. In cold climates, about two-thirds of the average utility bill goes toward heating! For most people, the heating and cooling units are mechanical systems that need to be maintained and inspected by a professional every year. Here are a couple of strategies to keep in mind for maximizing operating efficiency.

Green Strategies for Maintaining Your Mechanical System (Action Item 4)

- Green Strategy I: Stay Warm
- Green Strategy II: Keep Cool

Green Strategy I: Stay Warm

No matter what kind of system you have, our top piece of advice for upgrading your heating is this: Use the Energy Star label to get the most efficient unit possible. If you own or plan to buy an older home, it probably has a forced-air system, which pushes warm or cool air through ductwork in your ceilings, or a boiler system, which uses hot water and radiators.

If you live in a colder climate and have ductwork, you likely have a furnace, which runs on oil, gas or electricity. The most-efficient units reuse some of the heat lost through escaping steam—these are called "condensing" units. Furnaces are rated in terms of their annual fuel utilization efficiency (AFUE), which is calculated as a percentage. (Yes, more rating systems!) Older furnaces often have an efficiency rating of around 65 percent, while newer models can be more than 90 percent efficient.

Boilers use oil or gas to heat water or steam that is distributed through radiators, baseboards, or pipes that run under your floor. This is called a radiant floor, and it's a great feature to add if you're doing a gut remodel in a cold climate. Old boilers can be really rickety, so a new boiler with a 99 percent AFUE rating could almost cut your heating bills in half.

Another great technology to consider for keeping your home warm is the heat pump. A heat pump is a device that pumps heat from one place to another. It generally works best in warmer climates and allows you to tap into natural sources of heating.

There are two main types of heat pumps available. The first type, air-source heat pumps, uses an evaporation and condensation cycle to extract heat from the outside air and bring it into your home. The second type, geothermal or ground-source heat pumps, uses the constant underground temperature of the earth to augment your heat system. Geothermal systems work by tapping into the constant 50-degree temperatures hundreds of feet underground. In the winter, this is a free source of heat (and in the summer, this can actually be a free source of cooling too). Remember, these pumps don't make sense for every home—your climate, the size of your lot, and local geology all affect whether geothermal is a possibility. It's best to ask an expert for help in determining if this type of system is right for you.

Green Strategy II: Keep Cool

If you're not paying a fortune to stay warm, then you may be paying a fortune to keep cool. In much of the country, life without air-conditioning is a sweaty, inconceivable prospect. Life with air conditioning can be made cheaper and cleaner if you follow a few simple rules. As always, start with a professional inspection. If you need to upgrade, then purchase an Energy Star model. The efficiency of air conditioners is measured by the seasonal energy-efficiency Ratio (SEER), which ranges, in this case, from 13 to 21. An Energy Star-rated, efficient, central air-conditioning unit will be rated at least 14. Our view is the higher the SEER rating, the better.

The same is not true when it comes to size. Bigger is not always better. Air conditioners are like shoes—too big is just as bad as too small. An oversized air conditioner is not only more expensive, it will short-cycle (turn off and on) more often than a right-sized unit, which is not an efficient way to operate. Think of a car that smoothly accelerates, rather than a hotrod that peels out at every intersection. Short-cycling is especially problematic in humid climates, where an oversized air conditioner will blast a home with arctic chill and quickly shut off without properly dehumidifying the home. The result is a clammy, meat-locker feel. Right-sized HVAC or cooling units are a key to saving money, saving energy, and keeping your home comfortable.

Over-sizing is distressingly common. A recent study conducted by the State of Arkansas found that 90 percent of newly built homes had oversized air-conditioning units. This results in higher monthly energy bills for the homeowners, and homebuilders incurring an average of $600 in unnecessary construction costs. We believe that finding the right-size HVAC unit is work best suited for an expert. So don't be bashful about getting the help you need before making this big ticket purchase.

Green Tips: Suggested Keys for Ongoing Mechanical Efficiency

1. Keep it in tune. Keep your HVAC system regularly maintained by a professional. Oil furnaces need to be cleaned and tuned up every year. Heat pumps, boilers and central air-conditioning systems should be serviced at least every other year.

2. Give your vents some space. Keep your air-supply vents, radiators and baseboards clean, uncluttered by furniture, and unblocked by drapes.

3. Temperature settings matter. The U.S. Department of Energy recommends setting your digital thermostat to 68 degrees when you're heating and 78 when you're cooling. When you're sleeping or away from home, those figures change to 55 degrees and 85 degrees. Be sure to use the correct settings on your digital thermostat to help you save money.

ACTION ITEM 5: WORK WITH NATURE

If the best things in life are free, here's another one: Let nature do its part to help you heat and cool your home free of charge. You can do this by incorporating a couple simple, no-cost strategies we're about to describe to you.

Real estate agent Craig Schriber, in Reno, Nevada, knows all the latest, greatest technological tricks for heightening home performance. His home has a geothermal heat system, which he's enhanced with a tighter building envelope, new insulation, and new low-e windows. But when he is out on the prowl for properties with his clients, he still pays a nod to the past. "I'll point out the simple things that the farmers and ranchers have been doing for a hundred years or more," he says. "I'll point out that one house has a pine tree in front, while another will have a deciduous tree, and it means that the one with the pine will be in shade all year. It's simple stuff, but it's important."

Modern technologies like insulation and mechanical systems are one way to keep your home comfortable. Passive techniques, however, offer a timeless way to achieve minimal cost heating and cooling. Don't discount the helpfulness of these two natural strategies for year-round comfort.

Green Strategies for Working with Nature (Action Item 5)
- Green Strategy I: Take Advantage of Natural Heating Techniques
- Green Strategy II: Incorporate Natural Cooling Methods

Green Strategy I: Take Advantage of Natural Heating Techniques

Dale and Pat Bulla live in the hills outside Austin, Texas. Austin is a green, hilly, humid part of the Lone Star State that at times can feel hotter than a Tabasco-dipped jalapeño on a habanera sidewalk. The sun is usually scorching during the summer. Still, the Bullas wanted to own a home filled with natural light so they could appreciate their large native garden from any direction. Their goal was to make sure the sun stayed out of their home during the brutal summer months, but streamed in during the chilly winters.

When they built their home, they developed the living room as a long rectangle. The north and south walls were nearly continuous glass. The east and west were nearly windowless. Over the south-facing windows, they placed awnings precisely calibrated to keep the sun out during the summer and let it in during the winter. On a warm day at the end of September, Dale stood in his living room and pointed to a sliver of light falling across the carpet. "We are just at the tail end of summer," he says, "and the sun is lower in the sky. So, as you can see, the sunlight is just beginning to enter the house."

The Bullas' custom home took perfect advantage of natural heating. Also known as passive solar heating, natural heating is when the energy of the sunlight is used to warm a home. It typically involves three things. First, to take advantage of natural heating, light has to get into the home. That means a home will need the right type of sun exposure and windows to allow sunlight to enter. Second, the home will need thermal mass, a material that absorbs the heat from the sunlight. And finally, the home needs mechanical or passive ventilation (such as open windows, which costs you nothing!) to distribute the heat produced from the thermal mass.

Think of it this way: If you've ever walked over a cool floor on a hot summer day, you understand how materials like tile, stone, concrete, or brick can remain cool for a long time even when the sun is beating on them. This is called "thermal mass," the ability for dense materials to maintain their temperature and store heat for a long time. So, in layman's terms, thermal mass helps absorb heat to balance out the temperature of its environment. It softens temperature swings. For example, on a hot day, thermal mass will absorb heat. Later that night, when it's cool, the thermal mass will cool by releasing that stored heat. Ben Falk, a landscape architect in Vermont, uses exterior hardscaping features to soak up summer heat and extend the warmth a little longer into the winter. "The stonework around the pond is great thermal mass," he says. "The pond can store heat for weeks, so you extend your season into the fall."

Successful natural heating might be easier to achieve through thermal mass than you think. For instance, if you have a concrete slab foundation, consider stripping away the carpet and finishing the concrete. Because it's dense, the concrete will provide thermal mass. You can also get some of the same effect by adding plaster to your walls, using stone countertops, installing tile or even adding large plants with ceramic pots to sunny rooms.

To be successful with natural heating, there are two must-haves. First, you must have ample exposure to the sun through the right type of windows, ideally south-facing and located directly where the sunlight falls. Second, you must have thermal mass material that is thick enough to store the heat, but not so thick that it's always cool. In most places, 4 to 6 inches of thermal mass is ideal. We suggest you enlist the help of a passive solar design specialist to take advantage of natural heating in your home.

Green Tips: Make the Most of Natural Heating

1. Position is everything. The sun rises in the east and sets in the west. That means the most intense direct light will be on the eastern and (especially) western sides of the house. To maximize passive solar heating, your windows should be south-facing and thermal mass should be correctly positioned to absorb the heat.

2. Seasons matter. Natural heating is especially effective in the wintertime. As the sun traces its route across the southern sky, it is lower in the winter than it is in summer. That means that any south-facing windows that are shaded by the roofline in summer receive direct sun in the winter.

Green Strategy II: Incorporate Natural Cooling Methods

Natural cooling, also known as passive cooling, is an efficient way to reduce the amount of heat in your home. It's a simple ventilation process, much like the one we discussed in the inside zone. Yet, in addition to bringing fresh air into the home, it also replaces hot air with cooler air.

Today, so many of us are so used to turning on the air conditioner that we automatically reach for the thermostat when it's stuffy inside, even when it's cool and breezy outside. Natural cooling is a free solution you can tap into, and it works particularly well in areas with hot days and cool nights, like the

Here Comes the Sun!

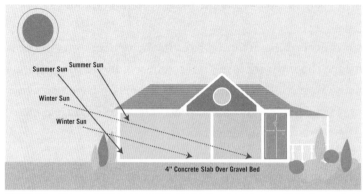

Figure 21 – How sunlight enters the rooms in a house can affect the home's ability to heat and cool.

mountains or the desert. You can open a couple of windows at night and wake up in the morning with cooler air throughout your home. And as a bonus, if you have thermal mass in your home, it will be cool and ready to soak up the heat of the day. To engage passive cooling, simply walk around your home, open your windows, and see which ones create a nice breeze when open.

You get the best breeze when you cross-ventilate, which means nothing more than opening windows on opposite sides of your home so the breeze can blow through. Not every home has a wall with an exterior window, so it might take some experimenting to figure out how you can get a breeze going through the entire place. Pay attention to the wind direction and intensity around your home, and then try opening different doors and windows on opposite sides of it. If you live in a tall home, you can open windows on the top floor to take advantage of the chimney effect, where warm air rises and is replaced by cooler air coming in below.

Consider ceiling fans. They're a great, affordable way to improve airflow inside your home and make you feel cooler by creating a breeze. Ceiling fans do not actually cool the air—they make the air feel cooler though. Which brings us to the ancient question of, "If a ceiling fan is on in a forest and there's no one there to feel it, does it keep anything cool?" The answer is no. Turn your fans off when you leave the room.

Look for ways to improve your efficiency by trying natural heating and cooling strategies in tandem with reduced use of your mechanical systems. You'll save energy and you'll save money. We hope you'll still have some energy left in your tank after tackling all these money-smart projects. Next, we're going to look at ways you can boost your health in the systems zone of your home. We'll focus on air quality in your ventilation system. Above all, you want to keep in mind that your ventilation system needs to stay clean and free of debris to perform well.

A HEALTHY SYSTEMS ZONE

As we learned in the inside zone in the last chapter, air has a huge impact on our health. In the systems zone, air moves through the ducts and vents of a ventilation system. A system's performance and overall energy efficiency depends on steady airflow.

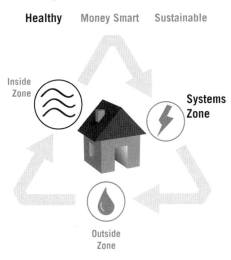

Figure 22 – Air is the focus of a healthy systems zone.

If there is a blockage, your system has to work harder. That takes energy, and energy costs you money. Let's take a look at how you can make your air in the systems zone healthy.

ACTION ITEM 6: OPTIMIZE YOUR VENTILATION SYSTEM

We hope you've already hired a professional to inspect, clean, and maintain your mechanical unit—typically an HVAC system with ductwork—to ensure high performance and good airflow. Just like your heating and cooling systems, improving your ventilation system is a simple task at its core. The key strategies to employ include regularly replacing your air filter and considering the addition of a whole-house ventilation system.

Green Strategies for Optimizing Your Ventilation System (Action Item 6)
- Green Strategy I: Change Your System's Air Filter
- Green Strategy II: Consider a Whole-House Ventilation System

Green Strategy I: Change Your System's Air Filter

Replacing your air filter regularly is a simple and money-smart way to help your system work a little more efficiently while simultaneously improving your air quality. If you have a forced-air system, a common type of air filter you may be familiar with is the 1-inch-thick kind used in an HVAC system's air-return duct, also called a furnace filter. We mentioned this filter in the inside zone and will now deepen our discussion.

When it comes to finding the right replacement filter, there is not one size that fits all. Instead, there is a rating scale to help you. Filters are rated according to the MERV scale, or minimum efficiency reporting value, which rates a filter according to the size of the particles it traps. A typical home filter is in the MERV 1-4 range, which will capture some of the larger particulates, like dust, in the air. You can upgrade all the way up to a MERV 11 filter, which will capture more of the allergens and particulates in your air, but these filters are more expensive and you will want to change them often. Read your ventilation system's instruction manual and consult with an HVAC expert to determine the best filter for your system and your needs.

Be sure to visually inspect your filters for nasty buildup. No matter how great a filter you might have, a clogged one can block airflow and hurt the performance of your entire system. Depending upon the type of filter you have and your household's sensitivity level to allergens, we recommend you change your filter every month, or every other month, as needed.

Green Strategy II: Consider a Whole-House Ventilation System

Keeping your air clean and ventilation system running smoothly doesn't end with a new filter. There are other options for you to consider, and whole-house ventilation is one of them. And it's a powerful choice if you're serious about systematically improving airflow through the systems zone of your home. The way it works is by drawing air out of the entire house the same way that a vent or fan works in your bathroom or kitchen. In this way, you might think of it as a giant spot ventilation fan for your entire home.

There are two main types of whole-house ventilation. One is the exhaust-only system, which is most appropriate for cold climates. It requires putting a specialized fan in the attic to push air out of the house and suck new air in through leaks in the building envelope in the walls and floors below. Leaks? Yes, even with all the sealing you've done, it's likely you still have tiny leaks inside your home. You can also use the same whole-house ventilation principle in reverse, which is called a supply-only system. Using power to draw air in, supply-only is recommended for hot, humid climates.

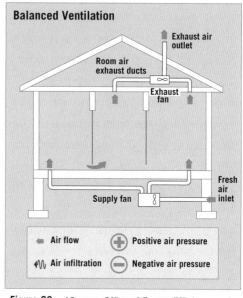

Figure 23 – (*Source: Office of Energy Efficiency and Renewable Energy, U.S. Department of Energy*)

Another type of whole-house ventilation is the balanced ventilation system. It's basically a fan at the top of the house, but with dedicated intake vents toward the bottom of the structure so you know exactly where your fresh air is coming from. The balanced ventilation system is more complicated to install than a simple fan in the attic for the exhaust-only system. It often requires changes to your existing HVAC ductwork. These upgrades can be a significant investment if you're not already doing an HVAC job or gut remodel. If you are doing an HVAC job, you might want to consider installing a mechanical ventilation system that is more effective and use it in tandem with the passive ventilation practices we covered earlier in this chapter. If you're interested in taking the mechanical route, we recommend you reach out to your agent and team of experts to find the best system for your home and budget.

To recap, when it comes to a healthy systems zone, the best way to achieve efficiency and ensure good air quality is to identify the air filter that's right for you and replace it regularly. This, in tandem with passive and mechanical ventilation, will help clean your air and keep it moving smoothly. If you're more adventurous and have the budget, look into whole-house or balanced ventilation systems. Let's now turn to sustainability, the final priority we'll cover in the systems zone.

A SUSTAINABLE SYSTEMS ZONE

In the systems zone, you can achieve great sustainability through reducing your water use. Water is a resource in severely short supply around the world. And, like energy, the cost of your water isn't likely to get any cheaper. Be smart and get a head start on what's coming.

In this day and age, there are countless ways that you can be smarter about your

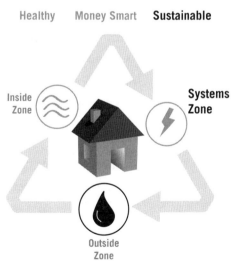

Healthy   Money Smart   **Sustainable**

Inside Zone

Systems Zone

Outside Zone

Figure 24 – Water efficiency is the focus of a sustainable systems zone.

conservation. It's true in each of the three zones of your home. When it comes to being sustainable about water use, we recommend you take simple measures. In the systems zone, your greatest water-conservation efforts can come from choosing smarter plumbing fixtures and appliances. It might surprise you that the greatest conservation opportunity of them all is our beloved toilet. Why? Because mostly anyone, anywhere has a toilet. And collectively, we flush them many times a day, which means we use millions of gallons of water. On the other hand, the most important appliance is our hot-water heater, which not only impacts our water usage, but our energy bill too.

ACTION ITEM 7: UPGRADE THE WATER-WISE WAY

If your goal is to become more sustainable in your systems zone, you'll want to put saving water at the top of your list. The good news is that there are numerous ways to accomplish this task and most involve pretty basic projects. You might choose to go it alone or you may need a plumbing professional to address the dirty work. Either way, we recommend you do four key things to help turn your systems zone into a water-conserving camel.

Green Strategies for Upgrading the Water-Wise Way (Action Item 7)
- Green Strategy I: Understand Your Water Bill
- Green Strategy II: Install Low-Flow Showerheads and Faucet Aerators
- Green Strategy III: Transform Your Toilet
- Green Strategy IV: Improve Your Hot-Water Heater

Green Strategy I: Understand Your Water Bill

Saving water begins by breaking out your water bill to get a sense of your monthly and yearly usage. Your water-use data may be provided in the same bills as your electricity. But in case you do not have your bills handy, contact your utility provider for access to your bills for the past twelve months. With your bills in hand, this exercise is just like the one you completed earlier in this chapter for assessing your energy use. You're now ready to focus on the portion of your utility bill that reflects water use.

Know that your overall water bill includes two categories: potable water and wastewater. Potable water includes the water you drink, cook with, or use to water your lawn; the wastewater component amounts to the water you use at home, like when you flush your toilet, do laundry, wash dishes, and shower. In general, wastewater cost is generally higher than what you pay for potable water because of a more involved collection and treatment process.

If you're on a municipal water supply, your water bill measures the amount of water you consume in units, typically in gallons or cubic feet. The same is true for the amount of wastewater you use. The cost of water varies widely and is usually determined by how close you live to abundant water sources, according to the nonprofit Circle of Blue (www.circleofblue.org). For example, the area of the United States closest to the Great Lakes has very low water costs, while more arid areas like Las Vegas, Nevada, and well-populated cities like Boston, Massachusetts, pay more.

We encourage you to study your bill and know how much water you actually use. You might be surprised. Depending on how much you use, the amount you pay may well keep in the same range every month. If you find some months where the price fluctuates greatly, make a note of it. It could be due to a leak you had to fix or to watering needs in your outside zone during particularly hot or dry months. Whatever the case, you want to bring your costs to a level that's sustainable and fairly predictable every month. It's not hard to do if you focus and make the changes we recommend.

Green Strategy II: Install Low-Flow Showerheads and Faucet Aerators

When it comes to water consumption in your home, you may think you are being conservative, but not really have an accurate idea about how much water you are truly using. Think about the morning shower you rely on to jump-start your day. Maybe you traded baths for showers once you learned how much less water a short shower requires than a full steaming-hot bath—up to 25 gallons for the average shower vs. up to 70 gallons needed for a bath, according to the Environmental Protection Agency. However, while you are struggling to wake up under that stream of hot water, there is a good chance you're still using more water than you need to use. That's why when it comes to showers, we recommend you replace older showerheads with low-flow attachments. A low-flow showerhead uses less water while it's maintaining good water pressure. According to the U.S. Department of Energy, any showerhead that was installed before 1992 is not likely to be low flow, so if your showerhead has been in use for that long, it would serve you well to update it. Not sure how old your showerhead is or if it is low flow? Measure its flow rate yourself by putting a bucket underneath it, turning it on to the pressure you'd normally shower with and filling the bucket until you have 1 gallon of water in it. If you've reached the gallon mark in less than twenty seconds, it's time to replace your showerhead.

Keep in mind that some low-flow units are better than others. While new showerheads cannot have a flow exceeding 2.5 gallons per minute (GPM), there are showerheads on the market with as little flow as 0.5 GPM. Think about how much less water you'll use and how much more money you'll save for that same morning shower if you're using one of those! Installing these low-flow showerheads is an ideal way to save water, save energy, and save money. *In fact, a household can save more than 2,300 gallons per year by doing so.* This equates to not only water saved, but less energy burned to heat the water and more money in your wallet.

When it comes to faucets, you want to install an aerator if you don't already have one. These inexpensive add-ons attach to the end of your faucet, slow the flow of water, and add air to maintain water pressure. An easy way to save water and money, aerators are worth installing anywhere you have a sink. We recommend you follow the U.S. Department of Energy's guidelines and purchase sink aerators with maximum flow rates of 1.0 GPM. Both low-flow showerheads and faucet aerators can be found at any home-improvement store. Just bring the piece you are replacing with you to the store to make sure you're buying the right size. As always, ask for help determining what you need or if you are uncomfortable installing either one of these money-smart options.

Green Strategy III: Transform Your Toilet

The EPA's WaterSense website states that American families use about 400 gallons of water a day. About 70 percent of that water is used inside the home. Of that 70 percent, we use the most water in the bathroom, especially with the toilet. The average person flushes the toilet 2,500 times a year—just imagine the number of flushes that adds up to in a lifetime! So with that in mind, it's time to transform your home's toilets from water-wasters into water-misers.

The first step is to look at the number of toilets you have in your home. For most homeowners, that number is two or three toilets. You want to check each of your toilets for their age and tank size. Do you have the older guzzling toilet types or the modern, efficient WaterSense low-flow or dual-flush units that run on very little water? If you don't know what kind of toilet you have, or its age, ask your agent or a plumbing professional for help.

Next, we recommend two options. First, you can upgrade to a low-flow unit with a WaterSense label. Low-flow units use three-quarters less water than a standard older toilet. Often, rebates or incentives are available from local municipalities to support the replacement of less-efficient toilets.

If replacing your toilet is out of the picture for now, make sure it doesn't use a ton of water per flush and that it doesn't run or leak. Testing for this is simpler than you think. You can place a brick or a 2-liter plastic bottle filled with water in your toilet's water tank. The volume of these objects means less water will be needed to fill your tank. Voilá! You've just created your own low-flow toilet. On the other hand, if you have a leaky or runny toilet, you'll want a plumbing professional to address it immediately. Ask your agent for a referral.

Green Strategy IV: Improve Your Hot-Water Heater

The low-hanging fruit is to have your hot water heater inspected and maintained every year. We recommend you lower the temperature of your water heater by at least 2 degrees and insulate your unit. Something as easy as a hot-water heater insulation blanket should do the trick. You can get one from your utility company or off the shelf at your local home-improvement store for a very reasonable price. If you have an older unit that's on its last leg, we recommend you replace it with an Energy Star unit. Because you use it so often, an efficient hot-water heater can start paying you back sooner than other appliances. A more expensive option is a tankless or on-demand hot-water heater. These systems are great in that they require less energy than traditional ones and supply hot water at a moment's notice. While they're a testament to modern plumbing technology, their payback period is generally longer than an Energy Star unit due to the high purchase cost. On the other hand, an on-demand system brings comfort and might be a competitive advantage when you're ready to sell your home.

Green Tips: Conserving Water (and Energy) in the Systems Zone

1. Go low-flow. We promise your water won't flow out at a wimpy trickle if you install low-flow add-ons to your plumbing fixtures. Use WaterSense low-flow toilets in your bathrooms. Replace your showerheads with ones that run at 2.5 GPM or less. Add an aerator with a maximum flow rate of 1.0 GPM to the kitchen or bathroom faucet to reduce water flow.

2. Cheat if you have to. If you don't have it in your budget to upgrade to a low-flow or dual-flush toilet, put a brick or full 2-liter bottle in your toilet tank. These will take up volume and help you save water every time you flush.

3. Bring in the experts. Have a professional inspect and service your hot-water heater every year.

4. Make it cool, yet cozy. Turn down the temperature on your hot-water heater by at least 2 degrees and wrap your unit in a blanket.

We challenge you to pick some or all of the action items we've highlighted in this chapter to help get your systems to a place of peak performance. And we encourage you to enjoy the comfort and savings a money-smart, efficient home provides. As always, consult with your local team of experts and go for it!

CHAPTER 5:
THE OUTSIDE ZONE

*There must be a better way to make the things we want, a way that
doesn't spoil the sky, or the rain, or the land.*

Sir Paul McCartney

THE SPANGLERS' STORY: A TEACHING MOMENT

Sometimes it takes certain people longer than others to understand
the beauty and importance of water-wise, sustainable landscapes. When Jason
Spangler and his wife Lisa bought a new home in a suburb of Austin, Texas,
they opted for a xeriscaped yard. The term "xeriscape" comes from the ancient
Greek word *xeric*, which means dry. Xeriscaping involves using landscaping and
materials that are native to the location. In doing so, your yard will require less
water and fertilizer to encourage growth and sustainability.

"It was just the right thing to do," says Jason. "The traditional lawn has all these
problems—tons of water, pesticides, herbicides. I can't bring myself to have a
Bermuda grass lawn."

As they trucked in mulch and gravel and plants, they took care to plant the
species in beds with orderly paths, so it wouldn't disturb the sensibilities of
more conventional neighbors. They also wanted to make sure they met the

neighborhood rules requiring yards to be "cultivated, pruned, and free of trash and unsightly material."

Despite the couple's great efforts, the homeowners association issued a citation because the Spangler yard simply didn't look pruned. In response, Jason put together a packet of information about prairies, native landscaping, and wildlife habitat; he presented it before the neighborhood board. Not only did he win the right to keep his yard, a few months later he won Yard of the Month! Now, he says, butterfly gardens and native patches are becoming an increasingly common sight in the neighborhood.

Without question, yards have always been an expression of individual tastes. The National Gardening Association reported annual lawn and garden sales in the United States reached $35 billion in 2007; in 2009, the Canadian gardening and outdoor living market boasted a total revenue of 5.5 billion in Canadian dollars, according to ResearchandMarkets.com. In the past, most of these home gardeners would have been shooting for the same target—a flat green lawn, some colorful shrubs, maybe a troll or two. No longer. Many homeowners are taking a second look at their outside zone. To a green-minded homeowner, the possibilities are as exciting as they are many.

Prior to putting on your overalls, hat, and gardening gloves, it helps to put things in perspective with the 80/20 Principle. A carefully planned outside zone can add great value to your home in its curb appeal for future buyers. It also can conserve life's sustaining element and an increasing precious resource—water.

IN THE OUTSIDE ZONE: SUSTAINABILITY IS YOUR 20 PERCENT

Did you know that although water makes up 70 percent of the world, less than 1 percent is safe for drinking? Water is an element that demands our attention. That's why when it comes to conserving resources in the outside zone, the majority of our focus is going to be on water. And like other natural resources, water will likely continue to cost us more money as it becomes scarcer and our population grows. We need to make smarter choices about our water consumption, and we can start in our own backyard.

While sustainability is your 20 percent focus in the outside zone, you'll also have opportunities to make your outside zone money smart and healthy too. So as you read, continue creating your to-do list by circling the action items and corresponding strategies that you find appealing. Join us on this, the final zone in your Green Your Home adventure!

PROJECT 3: MASTER LIST FOR THE OUTSIDE ZONE

PRIORITY	ACTION ITEMS

Sustainability	1. Water Your Lawn More Efficiently
	   • *Be Water Wise*
	   • *Collect Your Rainwater*
	   • *Use Your Rainwater*
	
	2. Create a Sustainable Landscape
	   • *Landscape for Your Climate*
	   • *Choose Native Plants*
	   • *Be Wildlife-Friendly*

continued

PRIORITY	ACTION ITEMS (CONTINUED)

Sustainability	3. Plant a Garden of Your Own
	  • *Grow Your Food with a Contained, Raised-Bed Garden*
	  • *Compost to Create Organic Fertilizer*

Money Smart	4. Improve Your Energy Efficiency from the Outside In
	  • *Plant Shade Trees*
	  • *Add Awnings to Stay Cool*
	  • *Consider a Solar CPV Power System*

Healthy	5. Practice Safe Landscaping Techniques
	  • *Limit Toxic Chemicals and Opt for Organic Care*
	6. Bring Your Home Outside
	  • *Install Green-Friendly Outdoor Living Spaces*

Figure 25

CONTINUING STEP 3: BUILD YOUR GREEN PROJECT LIST IN THE OUTSIDE ZONE

You've already made green improvements to your inside zone and your systems zone. Congratulations! That was no small feat. In some ways, we think the outside zone can be the most tangibly satisfying one in which to work, because you get to connect with nature, get your hands dirty, and see the fruits of your labor.

In this chapter, we'll help you build your project master list and apply it to the outside zone of your home. Our aim is to guide you to making at least a few improvements that will result in better overall sustainability through water conservation, money-smart upgrades, and a healthy outdoor space that you can enjoy with your friends and family. We'll divide up the action items into three parts. The first part, our 20 percent, will begin with sustainability. Then we'll move to money-smart items, and finally, items that relate to a healthy outside zone. So with that in mind, let's go green your outside zone!

A SUSTAINABLE OUTSIDE ZONE

For the brown thumbs out there, fear not—we're here to help you develop more of a green one. It's not hard to change your landscape from a conventional cookie-cutter yard into one that expresses your creativity and commitment to a better neighborhood and even a better planet.

"Much of what passes as landscape design is focused on 'shrubbing' it up, adding color, and other visually limited aspects of design," says Ben Falk, a landscape designer in Vermont.

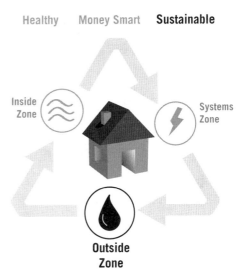

Figure 26 – Water efficiency is a key factor in the outside zone.

"That's nice, but that approach is not necessarily edible, soil-building, or wildlife attracting."

Falk adds that this approach also isn't the best option for capturing and storing solar energy or for being wholly responsive to the seasons.

To achieve a truly sustainable outside zone, we want you to focus first on your water consumption. Do you believe your current watering habits are efficient or wasteful? Do you believe that you are making the most of your outside zone? Through the three action items we're about to show you, we'll help guide you in both cases.

Three Action Items for Making Your Outside Zone More Sustainable

Action Item (1)   Water your lawn more efficiently.

Action Item (2)   Create a sustainable landscape.

Action Item (3)   Plant a garden of your own.

ACTION ITEM 1: WATER YOUR LAWN MORE EFFICIENTLY

Wherever you live in this great, diverse North American continent—the highlands, the lowlands, the mountains, or the plains—we can accurately predict one thing about your climate: Either you have too little water or you have too much. If you're really unlucky, you've got some of both—long stretches of drought punctuated by tumultuous downpours.

As you know, we humans are pretty good at engineering our outside environments. We've developed irrigation systems to get us through the dry summers, and storm-water systems to flush excess rainwater out of our yards and back into rivers and streams. However, as our cities have grown, our infrastructure doesn't work as well as it once did. A growing number of cities face seasonal water shortages, flooding, or both. Our storm-water systems were built when our cities were much smaller. Today, they are too old and often too small to manage the amount of polluted water that now runs off our driveways and roofs. As you consider ways to improve your outside zone, we suggest you consider landscaping choices that make use of less water. Let's start by taking a look at ways to use water more efficiently in your lawn.

Green Strategies for Watering Your Lawn More Efficiently (Action Item 1)

- Green Strategy I: Be Water Wise
- Green Strategy II: Collect Your Rainwater
- Green Strategy III: Use Your Rainwater

Green Strategy I: Be Water Wise

Water-wise landscaping doesn't have to mean giving up the grass you love. But with at least half of most municipal water sucked up by grass, sustainable lawn care does demand a certain level of respect for and responsibility to your neighbors and your community.

Green Tips: How to Care for Your Lawn Like a Good Neighbor

1. Water deeply, but infrequently. The problem with light daily watering is that your grass never develops a thick, hardy root system. It may sound counterintuitive, but less-frequent watering encourages stronger, healthier growth. A good rule of thumb is to wait until the grass fails to spring back up when you step on it. At that point, you want to give your lawn a deep watering.

2. Water early or late in the day. If you water when it's hot outside, much of the water will simply evaporate into the air. Instead, water early in the morning before the sun gets high in the sky or late in the evening, just before sunset, to maximize absorption.

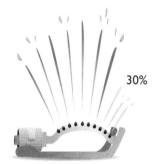

30%

Figure 27 – You can lose up to 30 percent of your water to evaporation if you water midday, vs. in the early morning or evening.
Source: EPA

3. Use the right amount of water. What's right in your area? You can find out by checking with your local utility provider or municipal government for recommended watering depths, or even buying a fancy evapotranspiration meter from your local hardware or home-improvement store. The right depth will vary from place to place, but you shouldn't need to water more than about an inch a week. To find out how long it takes for your system to water an inch, put a few glasses or cans around the yard, turn on the system, and use a ruler

to measure the water that accumulates. If you've got water running off the lawn, turn down the pressure; it'll minimize waste and help keep pollutants out of the storm sewers.

4. Don't mist. Fine mist is great for your leaves of salad but poor for your blades of grass. An irrigation system that delivers big drops of water low to the ground is far more effective and loses far less water to evaporation than one that sprays fine mist everywhere.

5. Install the right sprinkler system. If you are installing an automatic sprinkler system, make it clear to your installer that water conservation is a priority. Unless you want to manage the system yourself, consider features such as timers, rain/freeze sensors, and soil moisture monitors to help achieve that goal.

6. Fix poor aim. If you use a manual sprinkler or handheld hose, keep the water pointed at the soil. Watering your driveway will, at best, grow weeds and dandelions in the cracks and, at worst, can lead to structural damage and decay.

7. Fix leaks. Wet patches in the lawn are a sign of problems. If you have a leak in your irrigation system, talk to an irrigation professional and get your leak plugged right away.

By now, we hope you're considering installing a water-wise landscape because it aligns with one of your priorities for going green: leading a sustainable lifestyle. But your good citizenship reaps rewards for your neighbors as well. When people voluntarily choose to use less water, their cities are that much further away from investing in costly taxpayer-funded water treatment plants or implementing drastic watering restrictions. Your water choices may not seem like a big deal, but believe us when we say every drop adds up.

As a result, our governments have a strong incentive to help encourage people to use less water in their outside zones. In drier parts of North America, rebates are often available for water-wise landscaping. One program in southern Nevada, for example, will pay you $1.50 for every square foot of grass you remove; even Seattle, Washington, a city that gets a fair amount of rain, has a program that will pay up to $450 for an in-ground sprinkler system that includes an evapotranspiration or soil-moisture monitor. Other programs offer rebates for specific species of native plants. In Vancouver, British Columbia, the government encourages capture of storm water and offers rebates for rain barrels or rain gardens. With opportunities like these to be money smart while living sustainably, we think you should strongly consider going green in your yard and taking advantage of incentives that pay you for a landscape that's not only smart but beautiful too.

Green Strategy II: Collect Your Rainwater

Typically, when rain falls on the surface of your roof, two things can happen. If you don't have gutters, the rain will land on your roof and fall onto the ground below. If your home does have gutters, the rain channels into them, moves through your downspouts, and then drains in certain locations on the ground around your house. Either way, most of the water is lost to runoff. With a rainwater collection system, water can be captured for use in your landscape instead of being wasted.

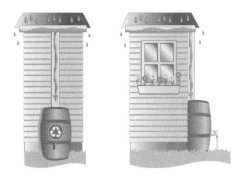

Figure 28 – A rainwater collection system is a great way to lower your water bill and generate water for landscaping and gardening.

A basic rainwater collection system requires a roof, gutters, downspouts (which help direct the water), and finally a storage container, such as a rain barrel, also known as a cistern. If you don't have gutters and downspouts, you will need to install them to successfully direct and collect your rainwater. If you already have them, you've got a great start. The one catch, however, is that depending upon where your gutters are placed, you may need to reconfigure them to effectively direct the flow of water from the roof to collect it effectively where you've placed the cistern.

Green Strategy III: Use Your Rainwater

Basic rainwater storage and usage couldn't be easier. Rain barrels can be very affordable, especially with local rebates often available. They come in a variety of cylindrical shapes, sizes, styles, and prices, starting at around $100. Many contain recycled plastic content, which is a sustainable bonus. Just make sure when you purchase a rain barrel, it comes with a spigot so that you can easily tap into the water you collect. To use the water for your yard or plants, you'll need either a hose that you can attach to your spigot, or a watering can that you can fill periodically. So you basically use the water just like you would for normal gardening. If you're unsure of what type of rainwater storage system will work best in your home, ask a rainwater collection specialist to guide you. Keep in mind that because the rainwater may contain contaminants and is not treated, you do not want to use it for drinking!

When it rains, a lot of the water sinks into the land, where it's naturally cleaned and filtered. Yet some of that water flows across the land and into nearby creeks, causing them at times to overflow. Thick vegetation covering the soil in your neighborhood can slow that process.

Now, imagine the same rain falling on an asphalt parking lot. This time not a single drop sinks into the asphalt. Instead, puddles form, soaking up oil, chemicals, and bits of tire. Unable to sink into the asphalt, all of this polluted water flows into a storm drain. In some cities, this will go into the water treatment plant; in others, it will blast high-speed into the nearest stream, creating a dirty, eroding torrent.

It's a little creepy to think about, but most of our yards function a lot more like a parking lot. Our sidewalks, driveways, and even most species of grass aren't very good at soaking up and filtering water. Instead, they create runoff that carries all sorts of pet waste and landscape chemicals with it downstream. That's why many sustainably minded homeowners build their landscapes with an eye toward replicating the processes you'd find in nature. They want to slow the storm water and clean out the pollutants.

"The whole idea is to bring back elements that act like nature, but still allow you to have a house and a driveway and everything else," says Tom Liptan, an ecologist with the City of Portland. "It's using plants to manage water. The more you plant, the more storm water you'll manage."

ACTION ITEM 2: CREATE A SUSTAINABLE LANDSCAPE

At this point, your outside zone is really shaping up in a sustainable way. You've taken steps to make it water wise, such as by installing rain barrels to collect the rain and maybe establishing a pretty (or even terribly ugly) rain garden. Next, we'll give you three strategies to continue your quest for a sustainable outside zone. First, we'll look at techniques for landscaping with your climate in mind. Then, we'll help you choose native plants to incorporate. And finally, we'll consider ways to attract wildlife to your yard. It's a fun adventure, we promise!

Green Strategies for Creating a Sustainable Landscape (Action Item 2)

- Green Strategy I: Landscape for Your Climate
- Green Strategy II: Choose Native Plants
- Green Strategy III: Be Wildlife-Friendly

Green Strategy I: Landscape for Your Climate

You don't have to live in the middle of the New Mexico desert to take advantage of the principles of xeriscaping. This type of drought-tolerant landscape design is becoming increasingly popular for reasons we've already mentioned: Water is expensive and plant cultivation can be demanding. Xeriscape landscapes are advantageous because they require little water and, once established, little maintenance.

"When I started out all you'd see is what we call 'zero-scaping,'" says New Mexico landscape designer Hunter Ten Broeck. "It was all gravel with maybe a yucca or something. True xeriscape is full of plants. It's got different colors, different textures, different areas of interest at different times of year."

The U.S. National Arboretum (www.usna.usda.gov) offers a hardiness zone map to help gardeners in North America determine which plants, grasses and trees will work best in their respective climates. The map shows average low and high temperatures in each zone.

If your sole purpose is to not water or mow a lawn, then sure, a minimalist rock garden will probably do the trick. Then again, it won't attract wildlife, shade your home, or provide a peaceful respite from the bustle outside. That's what Hunter created when he tore out the quarter-acre of Bermuda grass surrounding his home and installed a flourishing landscape that, as he puts it, "looks like Albuquerque." He kept a small patch of grass. It's a slow-growing species he mows once a year. Mostly, he just enjoys the yard by watching it grow.

"My wife and I sit in the backyard almost every evening. We have an old cottonwood tree that's probably 40 or 50 feet tall and birdfeeders. I've seen 25 or 30 species of birds in our yard," he says. "Even though it's in the center of Albuquerque, it feels like we're in a remote meadow somewhere. I'm someone who likes to hike, and I love to create a little of that space and feeling, in my own yard."

Green Tips: Principles of Sustainable Landscaping

1. Have a plan. For aesthetic reasons, this is essential to any home landscape. But if you're trying to wring the most out of every drop, careful planning will give you the best results.

2. Know your soil. Many areas have different combinations of clay, sand, and other materials. You need to either match your plants to the soil you already have, or amend your soil to match the plants you want to see. If your home was recently built, it probably lacks deep, rich soil and will need to be improved. If you need help, ask a professional at a local nursery for her advice.

3. Irrigate efficiently. Xeriscape isn't about not using water—it's about not wasting water. Unless you're into the minimalist look, your greatest xeriscape triumphs will have a well-designed irrigation system that gets you the maximum foliage at the minimum cost. Drip systems or soaker hoses do the best job delivering water straight to thirsty roots. And make sure you don't overwater! It's the easiest way to kill a beautiful landscape.

4. Plant appropriate species. Your local nursery will be able to advise on the best native, drought-tolerant plants. Do some research and ask your friends and neighbors about plants that work well for them. You can also attend local gardening workshops for help.

5. Plant in zones. Place species with similar water and soil needs in similar places, where you can drip or ooze the perfect amount of water onto their roots.

6. Mulch deeply. 4 inches of wood chips or 2 inches of rock keep the soil underneath moist and cozy—cool in summer and warm in winter.

7. Minimize your grass area. Dazzle your neighbors with a fabulous, sustainable landscape of year-round fascination. Mix your landscape of drought-tolerant natives with dedicated grass areas, patios, or spaces you can use for outdoor living.

Green Strategy II: Choose Native Plants

Proper plant selection is critical to creating a sustainable landscape. And perhaps nothing is more important than choosing native plants, those that are local or indigenous to your area. The great thing about native plants is that they are relatively easy to maintain. Also, they tend to not only survive, but thrive under normal local conditions. Native plants are truly sustainable because they require little help. For the most part, with good sunlight, soil, and water, they take care of themselves.

As wonderful and sustainable as native plants are, there are also nonnative plants we recommend you avoid on this part of your green adventure. These are called invasive plants. The problem with invasive plants is that because they have no local competition from other plants or pests, once established, they can grow very quickly, take over the landscape, and kill off the local or native plants. One well-known example of an international invasive plant wreaking havoc on local ecosystems is the "foot-a-night" vine, kudzu. Originally native to the Far East, kudzu has flourished in the southeastern region of the United States and has even been found as far north as Leamington, Ontario. While this plant is not native to North America, it has thrived at the expense of local plant life.

If you want to know more about native plants, those local to where you live, stop by a neighborhood nursery and ask for advice. You can also do a lot of research online about the best plants for your area. Whatever you do, it's worth taking a little time to figure out the best possible choices. Plants, like anything else in your home, are an investment of time and money, and selecting the right type of native plants will save you a headache.

Green Strategy III: Be Wildlife-Friendly

Diana Guidry, a homeowner in Florida, saw opportunity in destruction. When a hurricane tore out all the trees in her yard and wiped out most of her plants, Diana decided it was time for a change. She got out her shovel and started planting native Floridian plants that were not only more likely to survive the next hurricane, but would also fill her yard with wildlife. She created a thick, natural landscape of trees, shrubs, and groundcover. In no time, her yard became home to seventeen different butterfly species.

"I feel very strongly about having a landscape that supports the local wildlife," she says. "It looks delightful, and it's something I can feel good about."

Diana is not alone in her conviction. Many of us are realizing that in taming the wild to make homes for ourselves, we've neglected to preserve the homes of the critters who lived there before us. According to the Audubon Society, many common North American bird species, such as meadowlarks, are in steep decline due to the loss of habitat and to toxic pesticides that poison them and the bugs and fish they eat. Wildlife-friendly landscaping is good for the yard and garden too. It helps control pests and encourages seeding and pollination.

Green Tips: Ideas for Making Your Landscape More Wildlife-Friendly

1. Cover. While a typical yard is largely flat, a wildlife-friendly landscape will emphasize vertical layers: trees, bushes, shrubs, and groundcovers that birds and animals can hide in. Arranged around the perimeter of the yard, these plantings can also provide a much more attractive barrier to the world outside than a plain old privacy fence, and they create a sense of being enclosed in a remote wilderness.

2. Food. Nuts, seeds, berries, and nectar all tempt different varieties of animals. Locally owned nurseries, your municipality, area gardening clubs, or local chapters of organizations such as the National Wildlife Federation or Audubon Society typically publish lists of plants that local or migrating critters find irresistible.

3. Water. Humans aren't the only ones who like the sound of trickling water. Adding a small pond or fountain to your landscape will entice even more animals to come take a dip. You can purchase a water garden at your local home-improvement store.

4. Places to raise young. Bird houses, nesting boxes and natural shrubby areas all entice animals to not only stop by, but to stake out a home. There's nothing like waking up to the sound of a singing songbird and her backup choir.

Because wildlife-friendly habitats tend to be resilient and climate-adapted, they will address many of the other environmental challenges posed by a typical yard. As Florida homeowner Marilyn Barber puts it, "Creating a habitat garden was something I had to do for myself, my children, and my grandchildren. As I sit here, I can see all these beautiful plants. I'm not looking at grass, something that needs water and pesticides to stay alive. It's enriching to create a habitat that's peaceful and shaded and quiet, with the butterflies and birds flying around."

ACTION ITEM 3: PLANT A GARDEN OF YOUR OWN

Gardening can be as simple or involved as you want it to be. Our goal is to give you a little knowledge and a few projects to get you moving on your path toward sustainability. A garden is such a great addition to almost any outside zone, because it enables you to experience something timeless, to be creative, and to connect with nature. Best of all, you get to enjoy the fruits—and the vegetables!—of your labor.

Before you break out the gardening gloves, you need to know a little about the planning that goes into creating a garden. You'll need to consider the seasons that affect when you'll be able to plant, the space where you're going to plant and, probably the most obvious consideration, what you'll grow. So let's get gardening.

Green Strategies for Planting a Garden (Action Item 3)

- Green Strategy I: Grow Your Food with a Contained, Raised-Bed Garden
- Green Strategy II: Compost to Create Organic Fertilizer

Green Strategy I: Grow Your Food with a Contained, Raised-Bed Garden

A contained, raised-bed garden is advantageous because it allows you to introduce high-quality soil from the start, rather than working with the existing soil in your yard, which could be of poor quality or even toxic due to pesticides or prior uses that weren't sanitary. Because of their ideal growing conditions, container gardens tend to require less water and produce fewer weeds and more fruitful plants.

You can purchase containers at your local garden supply store, or build your own. If you take the do-it-yourself approach, there are several green (read: sustainable) options in selecting your building materials. If you prefer wood, go for the most rot-resistant species, such as cypress, cedar, or redwood, says

Craig Jenkins-Sutton, a landscape designer in Chicago, Illinois. Also, choose wood that is certified by the Forest Stewardship Council (FSC), which means that it was harvested in a sustainable fashion.

"If you choose treated wood, make sure that the treatment is not harmful or will not leach into the surrounding soil," Craig says, noting that pressure-treated and stained products can contain harmful chemicals.

Figure 29 – A contained, raised-bed garden allows you to use high-quality soil, requiring less water.

Stone is another green option in constructing a container garden, especially if you repurpose broken sidewalk pavers or stepping-stones to build your garden walls. In determining its location, you'll want to position the container in your yard so that it receives six to eight hours of direct sunlight every day during growing season.

Methods vary on how to construct the floor of your container garden. If you're concerned about soil contamination or invasive weed species on the site where you are constructing your container, use a heavy-duty weed barrier. Otherwise, the preparation can be as simple as installing the raised bed directly on top of the existing grass or soil, says Craig. He recommends loosening the ground soil first to allow for better drainage. You also can build container gardens on concrete surfaces, but it's highly recommended that you fracture the surface before building the container garden to ensure proper drainage.

The ideal dimensions for a container garden depend on what you're growing and how much space you have in your yard for a garden. Pay particular attention to depth, because the container must accommodate the root zones of your chosen plants. Eighty percent to 90 percent of plant roots exist in the top 24 inches of available soil volume, according to Dean Hill, a landscape designer in Los Angeles, California.

"Plant roots typically spread out horizontally, not vertically," he says. "A good rule of thumb is to make raised planting beds between 18 and 24 inches deep. A vegetable garden, specifically, can be 12 and 18 inches deep if it will only be used seasonally."

What type of soil you use is as equally important as how much soil you use. The type of soil will depend on the type of plants. Rich Radford, a garden designer in San Francisco, California, breaks it down as follows:

- Vegetable gardens need well-tilled soil with high nitrogen content and lots of composted organic matter.

- Mediterranean plants or drought-tolerant plantings require well-drained sandy/loam or gravely soil.

To simplify matters, you can opt to purchase soil that is specifically blended for raised beds at your local garden supply store. "Most hardscape suppliers will have their own custom blends that can include everything from compost to aged manure to sand," says Craig. "Make sure that the soil has a large percentage of organic material as it helps to retain water and keep the soil from compacting, and it provides nutrients to the plants."

However, Rich warns against filling the planter exclusively with soil that has a high percentage of composting organic matter, as the soil level will drop over time. Instead, he recommends using a compactable fill soil and then tilling in compost material into the top 12 to 18 inches.

Now, what you plant is determined by two things: what you'd like to grow and what you can grow at different times of the year, depending on where you live. There are vegetables that grow better in cooler weather, typically in very early spring when the soil is still cool. A few examples of cool-weather vegetables are lettuce, kale, cabbage, broccoli, and cauliflower. Some vegetables grow better in warmer weather, typically in the early fall when the soil is warmer. Examples of vegetables you could plant in warmer periods are tomatoes, red bell peppers, squash, and beans. Every plant has different requirements, so be sure to follow the appropriate instructions when you buy the seeds.

Green Tips: Recommendations for Successful Gardening

1. Ask for advice. If you're stuck or confused, look no further than friends, family, and neighbors who are avid gardeners. They often have great tips and are happy to share their knowledge, success stories and even failures. You can also search online for more extensive information.

2. Tap local knowledge. Join a local gardening club and find out which fruits and vegetables grow well in your area. You can network and trade ideas with other gardeners—maybe even some who live nearby.

3. Hire an expert. If you have it in your budget, consider hiring a professional gardener to consult with you and even install the entire project. Just be sure to take good notes and ask a lot of questions throughout the process. It's your money, so it's worth investing if you can learn from them for future projects you might do on your own.

4. Consider community gardening. If you don't have the space or the proper lighting for a garden in your own yard but want to enjoy its benefits, scope out a local community garden. Nowadays, these types of shared gardening plots are popping up everywhere.

5. Be prepared to share. Even small gardens can often produce more tomatoes, zucchini, or lettuce than you'll personally consume. Fresh-grown veggies make wonderful gifts ... that or investigate pickling and canning for later.

Green Strategy II: Compost to Create Organic Fertilizer

Another great idea you may consider undertaking when you look into planting a garden is creating your organic fertilizer by composting. Good soil is one of the keys to successful gardening, and good composting goes a long way toward this end. Composting is a process of turning some parts of your home's waste, like certain elements of ordinary garbage, into rich organic nutrients that are great for your garden. The compost you create boosts the strength of the soil, which in turn improves the quality of your vegetables.

Here's how we recommend you get started with your compost. You'll need a dedicated container placed in the shade that can drain easily to house the compost pile. For about $100, you can buy a good quality compost bin. We recommend checking out your local hardware or home improvement store for a sturdy and closed-lid version. One that tumbles is a plus. Once you've purchased a bin, the best way to start a compost pile is to begin by layering the materials. At the bottom of your pile, you want organic materials such as chemical-free grass clippings, organic soil, old leaves, and untreated woodchips. On top of that, you want to add a layer of scraps from your kitchen like coffee grounds, fruits, and vegetables. Add water and keep alternating the layers within the bin until you fill it up. Then, you'll need to turn the material with a shovel every now and then. If done correctly, the pile should heat up and eventually produce a nutrient-rich, soft brown-colored mixture. This is your usable compost, organic fertilizer that you'll add to your raised-bed garden. Decomposed compost may take a little time to create, but it's the best thing you can ever do for your garden.

Green Tips: Creating a Successful Compost Pile

1. Compost every day. Make it a practice of adding your fruit and vegetable scraps, eggshells, coffee grinds, and even tea bags to your compost pile every day. Collect these items in a jar and set a routine for taking them out to your compost bin every evening.

2. Compost no-no's. Avoid adding meats, fish, dairy products, waste from animals such as dogs and cats, and pesticide-laced yard trimmings like grass and plants.

3. Easy on the water. Water every now and then, but don't overwater your compost pile. The best way to check on your moisture level is to bravely stick your hand into the pile and feel it—you just want it to be damp, not waterlogged.

4. Shake it up, baby. Periodically agitate the pile by moving the layers around. You want to help the compost material decompose, and to do so, you need to ensure that it stays warm.

A MONEY-SMART OUTSIDE ZONE

As we learned in the systems zone in the last chapter, being money smart is an important priority that can influence the projects you choose to undertake on your green adventure. And when we talk about being money smart in the context of green, we are mostly talking about projects that save energy. Think back to the last chapter: The more energy you can save, the lower your bills. In the outside zone, being money smart with energy plays an important role as well. Things like planting shade trees in the appropriate place or adding awnings are easy and money-smart investments. Other projects, such as adding solar panels, are more complex and costly. Let's take a look at some ideas on how to make your outside zone as money smart as can be.

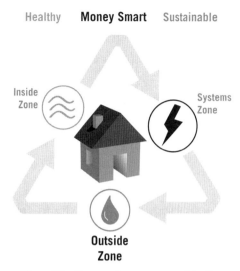

Inside Zone

Systems Zone

Outside Zone

Figure 30 – You can be money smart in the outside zone by taking on energy-efficient projects like planting shade trees, adding awnings, or installing a PV solar power system.

ACTION ITEM 4: IMPROVE YOUR ENERGY EFFICIENCY FROM THE OUTSIDE IN

The way we design our outside zones can play a huge role in making our homes more comfortable, durable, and efficient. As Ben Falk, a landscape designer who works in the damp, forested hills of Vermont, describes it, you want a yard that does more than just sit there looking pretty. "Our design approach focuses on the building-landscape system and sees the landscape as an extension of the house and part of the home," he says. "We want to draw people outside into the landscape as a living place, a sustaining place. And we want the landscape to aid in the performance of the building."

Sounds great, but where do you start? Here are some ideas to help point you in the right direction on your Green Your Home journey.

Green Strategies for Improving Your Energy Efficiency from the Outside In (Action Item 4)

- Green Strategy I: Plant Shade Trees
- Green Strategy II: Add Awnings to Stay Cool
- Green Strategy III: Consider a Solar CPV Power System

Green Strategy I: Plant Shade Trees

Planting shade trees can be one of the most gratifying projects you can undertake in your outside zone. Not only are you improving the air quality around you (plants absorb carbon dioxide and emit oxygen), but you are planting money savers in the process. Remember that trees don't grow to their largest potential overnight, but smaller, younger trees do tend to do well when planted and cared for according to their instructions. Keep in mind that trees require a good deal of water once you plant them. And once they're established, trees are fairly easy to maintain.

Location is critical when it comes to planting trees for shade. You want to add trees to the east and west sides of your property and at a safe distance from the front of your windows for the greatest benefit. Trees planted on the east and west will provide protection from heat and sunlight in the summer. The tree type you choose is important too. Deciduous trees, which lose their leaves in the late fall, are great because they allow that same heat and sunlight into your home in the winter. Remember to plant shade trees to protect your outdoor air-conditioning unit while you're at it—the system will work better if it's not under a blazing sun. Don't forget to clean leaves and debris off the unit regularly for maximum efficiency. If you're in a humid climate, keep your shade trees and shrubs trimmed back from the house to deter moisture. Planting trees is no small feat and it's worth investing in landscape professionals to help you choose the right type of trees, plant them, and get the job done correctly.

Not only do planting trees save you money by improving your energy efficiency, but trees can also add value to a home. As a real estate agent, Gary Keller's first advice to homeowners was always to plant a tree. It's literally like growing money! Home buyers tend to stay in their homes for seven to ten years on average, according to the National Association of Realtors. The saplings you plant today can grow into a majestic enhancement of your home's curb appeal when it comes time to sell.

Green Strategy II: Add Awnings to Stay Cool

Another strategy for improving your energy efficiency from the outside-in is to install awnings over your windows. Awnings are coverings that can help save energy and add to the exterior charm of your home. You place them over windows to prevent heat and direct sunlight from entering the home. This helps your air conditioner work more efficiently during the dog days of summer. When the sun is lower in the sky in the wintertime, sunlight will still be able to enter through your windows and provide some added heat. Awnings come in a variety of styles, color, materials and at various prices. If these are of interest to you, make sure your homeowners association approves of awnings and look for deals at your home-improvement store.

Green Strategy III: Consider a Solar CPV Power System

Nothing says "home of the future" like an array of concentrated photovoltaic (CPV) panels on your roof. Pollution-free power from the sun! However, as much as the price of CPV panels has plunged in recent years, they remain an expensive investment. Many solar CPV systems approach the range of $10,000 or more for a single house. And while rebates are often available, it definitely warrants careful consideration whether CPV is right for you.

There's no guarantee you'll make the price of your panels back when you sell your home, so the first consideration should be whether you'll be in your home long enough to really enjoy them. If you are sticking around for a decade, it's certainly possible you'll recoup the panel price through reduced energy costs. The payback will be faster if you're in a market that offers local rebate programs. Dale and Pat Bulla of Austin, Texas, installed a $20,000 solar energy system that cost them only $4,000 after a local rebate and a federal tax credit. "Our electricity bills were already low from passive heating and cooling, but they were cut in half after we installed the solar panels," says Dale, who adds that now they have become "net producers," meaning they produce more energy than they use. "Last year, we produced 2,040 kilowatts more than we actually used," he continued. "On average, we produce 170 more kilowatts per month than we use. Our electric bill totaled $42.60 for the entire year of 2010, and this includes the $6-per-month service charge to send someone to the house to read the meter."

You should also consider your structure and site to ensure solar is a smart option. For one thing, it may seem obvious, but CPV panels require the sun. If your roof is shaded (a good goal in hot, sunny climates), solar will be harder. There are alternatives to putting the panels on your roof—they can go on the ground or the house exterior. You will want to talk to a solar panel installer to see what type, if any, of CPV panels would work for your home, both functionally and aesthetically.

A HEALTHY OUTSIDE ZONE

With the great action items we've covered in this chapter, we hope you're well on your way toward creating a more sustainable outside zone. These final action items will focus on improving the safety and beauty of your yard, while boosting your personal well-being and enjoyment. Let's continue our Green Your Home adventure in the outside zone.

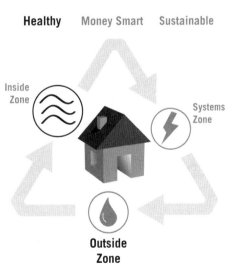

Figure 31 – Being healthy in the outside zone means choosing organic over chemical landscape care and breathing fresh air by bringing your home outside through hardscaping features, such as a patio or deck.

ACTION ITEM 5: PRACTICE SAFE LANDSCAPING TECHNIQUES

You've worked hard on making your outside zone as sustainable as can be and money smart too. It's also important to take steps to ensure you can enjoy your time outside with friends and family, knowing that your yard is free from dangerous chemical pesticides, herbicides, and synthetic fertilizers. If you're like us, we're sure you wonder how you can do this effectively. There are some scary statistics out there. According to a fact sheet published by the nonprofit group Beyond Pesticides, "Of 30 commonly used lawn pesticides, 13 are probable or possible carcinogens, 13 are linked with birth defects, 21 with reproductive effects, 15 with neurotoxicity, 26 with liver or kidney damage, 27 are sensitizers and/or irritants, and 11 have the potential to disrupt the endocrine system."

With all these health risks out there, it's no wonder you want to start practicing safe landscaping! Let's take a look at some ways to minimize toxic chemicals in your outside zone.

Green Strategy for Practicing Safe Landscaping Techniques (Action Item 5)
- Green Strategy I: Limit Toxic Chemicals and Opt for Organic Care

Green Strategy I: Limit Toxic Chemicals and Opt for Organic Care

If you have an outside zone, a yard that you want to enjoy with peace of mind, then here are the key questions you need to consider: Are you or your team of lawn care or gardening professionals using toxic chemicals on a regular basis in your yard? If so, what type of toxic pesticides do you use to control bugs? Which dangerous herbicides do you apply to pesky weeds? And do you treat your lawn with a chemical fertilizer? You can only know by checking the products you use or asking your team. There's no time like the present to find out. It might be the best thing you ever did for your health.

Once you answer these questions and know what you and your team of pros are using (and why), you'll want to look for organic treatment alternatives. That means you'll need to focus on healthy, more natural options to the dangerous chemical products. Nowadays, for every chemical or toxic product, there's an effective organic product that's safer for you, better for your plants, soil, and the local wildlife. That's not to say you'll never need another chemical product. At some point, you might have an issue that demands one, like a flea, tick, or fire ant infestation.

It's worth noting that nearly three-quarters of American households regularly use some sort of chemical insecticide, herbicide, or fungicide either inside or outside the home; in Canada, the figure is about a third. In both countries, these deadly chemicals are regulated by the federal government, so that when properly used, they shouldn't pose a health risk. But the concern that many health-minded consumers have is the "when properly used" part.

Because we're pretty sure we haven't reached the pinnacle of knowledge when it comes to the effects of pesticides, our government regulators are constantly reevaluating products to make sure they're still safe. If you opt for safer, organic options, you're setting yourself up for success in your outside zone without worry. Poisonous products should be the tool of last resort, not the default solution. And you should always use the least-toxic option. Some localities make the decision easy for you. For example, the Province of Quebec and more than seventy Canadian municipalities have already banned toxic pesticides.[*]

Green Tips: Maintain a Healthy and Pest-Free Yard

1. Use organic products and only apply pesticides if you have a serious pest problem. This may seem obvious, but many lawn services offer "preventive" spraying as a matter of course. Not only is this unnecessary, it may not even be effective—particularly if several chemicals with competing purposes are being used at the same time. As the interest in less-toxic living grows, many landscape services are now offering organic pre-emergent options, and we suggest you ask about the opportunities available. For smaller jobs, nontoxic options are available off the shelf from a home-improvement store or at your local nursery.

2. If you do have a serious pest problem, use the least-toxic solution. In both the United States and Canada, pesticides are labeled with four levels: caution, warning, danger, and danger-poison (in case it isn't obvious, the "danger poison" level of product deserves the most

---

[*]   "Quebec beefs up pesticide ban," Canada.com. April 4, 2006.

distance). Canadians can search specific products via Health Canada at www.hc-sc.gc.ca/cps-spc/pest/index-eng.php. In the United States, citizens can check out the National Pesticide Information Center at http://npic.orst.edu/index.html.

3. If you must use a harmful chemical, use it correctly. And that means down to every last letter. If the product label says to wear long sleeves and a mask, do it. Don't eat or smoke when you've been spraying, and don't spray near water sources or wells. Store and dispose of chemicals properly (that is, not by dumping them down the drain, but instead by taking the products to a hazardous materials waste drop-off). And then wash, wash, wash everything you've had anywhere in the vicinity of the stuff.

4. Modify your environment to make it less attractive to pests. If you have plants in your yard that need chemicals to keep from keeling over, maybe it's time to replace these plants with healthier, native green, pest-tolerant options. Do your homework and consult with your local garden center pros about the best plants for your landscape. Remember, you want low-maintenance, water-efficient options that hold up well against pests. Otherwise, you'll be fighting an uphill battle.

ACTION ITEM 6: BRING YOUR HOME OUTSIDE

It's common knowledge that spending time outdoors and getting some fresh air can do wonders for one's mood. As you continue on this green adventure, we recommend you take a look at your outside zone and consider ways that the space can be used to maximize your time outdoors.

There are many outdoor living options to consider, and we'll discuss a few possibilities below. We recommend talking to an expert about installing hardscaping or decking that is the right fit for your home.

Green Strategy for Bringing Your Home Outside (Action Item 6)

- Green Strategy I: Install Green-Friendly Outdoor Living Spaces

Green Strategy I: Install Green-Friendly Outdoor Living Spaces

So you've started daydreaming of relaxing in your backyard with a cold drink in hand after a hard day of work. You might be thinking about installing a deck, a patio or some other type of hardscape. Before undertaking any major improvements to your yard, think about how you plan to spend the majority of your time outside, whether it's barbecuing for your family or spending hours at a time working in your garden. Your vision will influence the size and design of the living spaces you ultimately build. Consult design books or consider sharing your thoughts with a home-improvement contractor or landscape architect to see what they suggest is the best use of the area you have.

If you're interested in building a new deck, there is one simple rule to follow: Start with lumber that is certified by the Forest Stewardship Council (FSC), which means that it was harvested responsibly. Some options include wood that is naturally resistant to bugs and rot, such as redwood, cedar, or FSC-certified ipe, also known as ironwood. Plastic lumber, which is becoming more prevalent, can be infinitely recycled at the end of its lifecycle says Los Angeles, California, landscape designer Dean Hill. However, he warns that if you go this route, choose a product with the highest amount of recycled content possible to avoid the significant carbon footprint associated with virgin material.

Rich Radford, a landscape designer in San Francisco, California, adds: "The key to sustainable deck design and build is creating a structure that will endure the lifestyle of the homeowner and the microclimate. Try not to use a product that requires annual refinishing or staining."

Rich says that longevity of design is also important when it comes to patios.

"A well-designed patio should be one that fits with the overall aesthetics of the garden or home, which, therefore, limits the possibility that a future owner will want to remove the feature and replace it," he says. "When we design and build hardscaping, we want it to last for generations of homeowners."

Material selection for patios is paramount to ensure the structure is green friendly. The biggest issue with patios is that traditionally they have been nonpermeable.

"In highly developed areas—think suburban and urban environments—any reduction in permeable surface can significantly increase the amount of rainwater runoff," says Craig Jenkins-Sutton, a landscape designer in Chicago, Illinois. "This additional burden has to be absorbed by storm sewers and water treatment facilities that were not designed to handle the increase."

Fortunately, there are several permeable building products now on the market, such as pavers that contain high amounts of recycled glass, recycled rubber, and even fly ash. The most sustainable choice would be a recycled, locally sourced material. Dean suggests recycled brick or concrete from a nearby source.

"These materials would typically be 'landfilled' from demolition projects, but they can be very effective when sensitively reused into current projects," Dean says, adding that stone from a local quarry is also an option for patio construction.

A word of caution: Have a design-build professional evaluate the ground composition of your building site prior to construction. "If your soil is slow draining, such as a heavy clay soil, a permeable paving installation may not be the right choice for you," Craig says. "If the water doesn't drain from the 'storage' area beneath the pavers, you are, in effect, creating an in-ground swimming pool.

"If you live in a northern climate, when that (in-ground) water freezes in the winter, the patio will heave significantly," Craig continues. "This will create a difficult surface to walk across during the winter and will often require that the patio be re-leveled in the spring."

If you don't have the space for an expansive deck or patio, consider installing other hardscape options to define your outdoor spaces.

Rich says he has reused all kinds of materials in unexpected ways to create defined spaces, privacy, and visual interest: an old claw-foot tub is repurposed as a raised container garden; construction debris—to include lumber, old pipe fittings, and metal hardware—is used to build a garden arbor; house siding is used to build a fence; and broken cement pavers are used to outline flower beds and gardening areas.

Regardless of the outdoor living space you choose, talk to a home-improvement contractor or landscape architect about what will work best for your outdoor space.

A SUSTAINABLE OUTSIDE ZONE IS A FEW ACTION ITEMS AWAY

With so many exciting ways to make your outside zone more sustainable, money smart, and healthy, we understand the desire to jump right in and get started. But like any other aspect of greening your home, we encourage you to take the time to plan it right. And if you need help in achieving your dream great outdoors, don't be afraid to reach out to your team of experts for advice. Rest assured, a few patches of well-designed and well-planned splendor are better than an entire yard of mediocrity. As your outside zone flourishes, you'll likely become an inspiration to your neighbors.

CHAPTER 6:
COMPLETE THE GREEN YOUR HOME TRANSFORMATION

I often quote an African proverb that says: "The world is not ours, the earth is not ours. It's a treasure we hold in trust for future generations." And I often hope we will be worthy of that trust.

KOFI ANNAN, FORMER SECRETARY-GENERAL OF THE UNITED NATIONS

ANNA'S STORY: GETTING IT DONE THROUGH DIY AND DELEGATION

Anna Weier was 27 years old when she bought her Winnipeg, Manitoba, home for $27,000. For that bargain price, the home needed more than just a little work. It stood vacant for nearly a decade, the plumbing was cracked, the electricity disconnected, and the whole place felt completely uninhabitable. Instead of running away from a potential nightmare, Anna saw opportunity and green potential.

Anna was not the kind of person who had experience pounding nails. She'd pitched in on minor improvement projects in the past, but heavy renovation was a completely new game to her. After purchasing her home, Anna decided she'd dedicate a year to getting it in the best shape possible. She enlisted resources and help through other graduate students, a local nonprofit, and her family.

Anna did several things to turn her green project list into a reality. She carefully consulted with her team of experts to plan the work and to better understand the process and costs. That helped give her confidence to choose the action items she would do herself and those she would need the experts to tackle. It also helped her stay within her budget. As a result of her diligent planning, when it came time to do the work, she and her team were able to simultaneously lay the groundwork for future improvements. For example, they installed the piping and wiring to make the house solar-ready while the walls were open, which will save time and money on upgrades in the years to come.

"Being involved in your home-improvement process does make things easier in the long run," says Anna. "I know where things are in the house and how to fix some of the things that come up. Even for hanging pictures, I know the composition of my wall. On the first floor, I know which walls have thicker drywall and how thick the rigid insulation is. It's nice to know."

We can follow Anna's lead when turning our green project lists into plans of action. Doing so is the most time- and budget-efficient way to ensure we address our priorities when we plan our improvements and get clear on what work needs to get done and in what order.

STEP 4: TURN YOUR PROJECT LIST INTO A PLAN OF ACTION

You've come a long way on this green journey and you're not done yet. Let's look back on the first three steps you took in the Green Your Home process. In step 1 you identified your green priorities. With step 2 you learned about your team of improvement experts. Step 3 walked you through the three green home zones and showed you action items to address the three green priorities. Now comes step 4, which will bring you even closer to the finish line.

In this step, you'll take your project list, the green improvements you want to make in each of the three green home zones, and turn it into a plan of action. Are you ready? Follow these four steps to buid your green action plan:

1. Create your list of action items for the home zones.

2. Organize your project list based on your priorities.

3. Make a realistic, comfortable budget.

4. Determine your time frame and team.

1. Create your list of action items for the home zones

Let's start by creating a list of all your desired Green Your Home action items. If you already have a finely tuned list in mind, skip to the next step. If not, you can refer to the master lists for each home zone on pp. 46, 94, and 141 to determine which items you would like to tackle.

2. Organize your project list based on your priorities

With your project list in hand, you now need to organize these action items into a workable sequence. This is actually easier than you think. All you need to do is get clear on the order of your priorities. And once you know what your top priority is, your action plan will start taking shape. Let's take a moment to revisit your priorities to ensure they're clear to you. Which of these is the most important? Second most important? And third most important?

With your priorities listed in terms of importance, the next order of business is to tie your list of action items to each of your priorities. Start with the items that address your first priority. Then add those related to your second priority. And finally, incorporate items relating to your third priority.

For your plan of action to be successful, stay focused on one priority at a time. So that means you can start by tackling the action items that fall under Priority No. 1 first. Move on to items for your second priority only after you've completed all (or at least most) of the ones related to your first priority. Once you've finished action items tied to your second priority, then it will be time to move on to Priority No. 3 and your last set of items. It's a simple, straightforward path to greening your home that works wonders. Keep your focus on one priority and one set of action items at a time and you will reap the rewards.

Connect Action Items to Your Priorities

Priority No. 1: _____ Priority No. 2: _____ Priority No. 3: _____

Action Items   Action Items   Action Items

_____   _____   _____

_____   _____   _____

_____   _____   _____

_____   _____   _____

_____   _____   _____

Figure 32

3. Make a realistic, comfortable budget

You've connected your list of action items to your priorities. And your items are organized so you can tackle the ones that tie to your No. 1 priority first. While you're well on your way to a successful "greenovation," you also have to make a budget that works for you. This means you need to figure out which action items on your list you can comfortably afford. Ultimately, only you know what you can afford, and with this number in mind, you'll know how much to budget for improvements each year. And that's an important point: You don't have to do all your items at one time. Think of your green journey not as a short sprint, but instead as a carefully planned long distance run that may extend over several years. Also, by spreading your costs over time, you'll have greater flexibility and minimize stress.

Another point worth considering is that for each action item you take on, there will likely be a cost for materials and labor. Will you buy the high-end product and work with the top local expert? Or will you opt for a low-priced product and a DIY approach? Maybe you'll find a comfortable place in between. You'll have options. And your costs will vary greatly depending on the scope of work.

4. Determine your time frame and team

Armed with a better sense for how to approach your budget, you also need to think about when you'll take on action items or hire a team to help you. As we've mentioned, home improvements may take more time than you think. A realistic plan is critical to your success. And since work in any of the three green home zones can involve equipment, people, and cost, we recommend you set expectations and get agreement in your household first. Then you can set some target dates more firmly on the calendar. And finally, you'll need to decide who will do the actual work. We recommend you leverage the knowledge of your agent to connect you to a network of experts that includes architects, design-builders, skilled tradespeople, and eco-consultants. Do you need to do every action item on your list? That depends upon your budget, your time, and your values.

FOUR KEYS TO KEEPING GREEN IN GOOD ORDER

Whether you do 99 percent of the green action items yourself or never even touch a tool, green home improvement provide an unparalleled opportunity to learn some of the most important things a homeowner can know: how homes work and how to keep them working well.

As you now understand, greening your home is a holistic process. It's about more than what kind of paint you put on the walls. It's a question of how healthy you can make your air quality. It's about making money-smart decisions that boost performance, and it's about a commitment to do more by using less while making things last for the long haul. You lay the foundations of the green process during your improvement, and you execute a green vision over your lifetime through diligent maintenance. Ongoing green is simple and it consists of four basic concepts.

Four Keys to Keeping Green in Good Order

1. Practice proper maintenance for optimal performance.

2. Keep it clean.

3. Watch for problems.

4. Share the rewards of your Green Your Home adventure.

1. Practice proper maintenance for optimal performance

Any mechanical system in your home requires ongoing maintenance, so if your green improvements include new ventilation, heating, air-conditioning, or other systems, make sure you know what they need. At a minimum, you'll have some air filters to inspect. And depending on which type of filter you prefer, you'll likely need to replace these several times a year. You'll also need to get your whole HVAC system serviced by a professional once a year.

Some appliances also require maintenance. It's recommended to vacuum out the vents in your clothes dryers and behind your refrigerator periodically to keep them running at their best. When you're recycling your old appliances and replacing them with new Energy Star ones, these ongoing needs are definitely something to pay attention to from day one. It's always worth calling your real estate agent—they provide support for life and can direct you to resources for your maintenance issues.

2. Keep it clean

Ah, cleanliness. This is something we recommend you factor in while you're making your choices of flooring and finishes. Dirt is not only the enemy of indoor air quality, but it also makes your mechanical systems work harder. Choosing finishes that are easy to keep clean, such as hardwood floors rather than carpets, will make things easier over the long term. But you also might make it a practice of leaving your shoes at the door—a time-honored tradition in many cultures around the world.

As a green homeowner, you probably don't want to choose any old cleaners to bring into your temple of purity. If you have a preference for nature's gifts, there are numerous recipes out there for effective home cleaning with vinegar, baking soda, citrus fruit, and other natural ingredients you can find around the house. You can also try some of the commercial products out there; anything touting the absence of phosphates, chlorine, or fragrances is a safe bet. We love the Mrs. Meyer's brand and there are many other all-natural products.

Cleanliness extends to the outside too. Cleaning out your gutters, getting leaves off of the roof, and making sure trees and bushes are trimmed away from the siding will help protect your home from moisture damage. And once in a while, give your windows a gentle scrubbing to help let the natural light enter. Yes, you'll need to clean up around your yard as well. But if you've planted native or adaptive species, you'll likely have minimized your landscaping and watering duties. A smart landscape does much of the work for you.

3. Watch for problems

As you now understand, homes develop problems when they're not functioning optimally. In essence, when water or air is escaping where it should be and is leaking into where it shouldn't be. If you haven't already, we expect you'll seal, spray, and stick everything together as tightly and diligently as possible, so you can look forward to a lifetime of hassle-free performance. But you can never be too sure.

Puddles and damp spots, either inside or in the yard near your home, are both possible signs of leaks. Insects, nature's graffiti artists, leave all sorts of droppings and residues. The key thing here is not to ignore signs that you've got the beginning of a problem. The last thing you want to do to your high-performing home is to put off a necessary maintenance job until it's too late.

4. Share the rewards of your Green Your Home adventure

It's clear that the choices you've made throughout this journey have put you on a path to a greener future. Without a doubt, this is a future you can be proud of. Not only have you decided to make changes that will support your health, save you money, and help the planet, but you've made a commitment to improvements that are in support of your values too. You know that greening your home does not just affect you. It is an adventure that has positive consequences for others around you as well. When family, friends, and neighbors see some of the changes you've made to your home and learn why you've decided to make these changes, you'll inspire them to begin their green adventures.

So just imagine: Here we are, standing in the doorway of your beautiful, updated green home. Maybe there are projects you look forward to accomplishing in the coming years. Maybe it's already perfect exactly as it is. Each of the homes you live in will be different: a different response to your unique climate, lifestyle, and values. But what we all hope you share at the end of your green home-improvement process is the satisfaction of knowing you've done something good for yourself, your family, and the rest of us as your neighbors. We also hope you feel pride, if not amazement, at all you've learned and accomplished. That's what

Anna Weier now feels in her beautiful Winnipeg home. "I look back on the process, and I look at my home and I say, 'Wow, I did that?'"

Above all, that's our message to you: *You can do it.* You can make your values take physical form. We wish you a smooth journey and a lifetime of joy and satisfaction in your green home.

APPENDIX: MORE GREEN YOUR HOME SUCCESSES

In writing this book, we came across so many fantastic accounts of Green Your Home adventures that it proved impossible to include them all. However, we understand how enlightening and educational it can be to read about others who have traveled the terrain before you. With that in mind, we have included three additional case studies that focus on the inside zone, systems zone, and outside zone, respectively. We hope these stories inspire as much as they inform.

THE INSIDE ZONE: SMALL STEPS CAN MAKE BIG DIFFERENCES

Green Your Home Adventurers:
Martin and Melissa Scanlan of Madison, Wisconsin

Their Home: A 1920s colonial home of about 1,200 square feet with two stories, tiny bedrooms, and an unfinished basement

Their Green Improvements

- High-efficiency, woodburning stove with a catalytic converter

- Ceiling fans

- High-efficiency appliances and furnace

- Low-VOC paints

- A finished-out basement that includes a living space, a bathroom, and a storage area

Their Story

Martin and Melissa Scanlan moved to Madison, Wisconsin, from California in 1999 and started shopping for their first home at the height of a housing boom. It seemed simply impossible to get anything under contract. The Scanlans decided to choose a home based on the neighborhood—somewhere walkable and bikeable where "we don't have to get in a car to go to the coffee shop." The existing design and condition of the homes they reviewed became secondary considerations because of cost. They finally landed a home that seemed in decent shape: It had aging appliances and needed cosmetic upgrades, but they were excited to move in and start tinkering.

Upgrading their home was a worthwhile adventure for the Scanlans. Martin and Melissa worked their way through a list of action items, and each one they undertook was determined based on their personal priorities. In the end, their consistent commitment to being healthy and money smart enabled them to focus on efficient and nontoxic options that resulted in a green home that proved its value in the marketplace.

Choose upgrades that accomplish multiple goals

Martin and Melissa's first investment was a woodburning stove for the main room. Not only would it help them stay warm during the cold winters, but they also liked the aesthetics of a woodstove. Their priorities of being healthy and money smart led them to choose an efficient one with a catalytic converter to remove particles from the smoke. (Untreated wood smoke is a powerful pollutant.) They also added ceiling fans to distribute the heat. The fans do double duty by removing the need for air-conditioning in the summer.

This dual approach was evident in all the upgrades made on their green journey. Replacing an old, clunky washer and dryer, as well as their furnace, with new, energy-efficient models reduced their utility bills dramatically, while opening up space in the basement for a living area.

"When things overlapped, it made it a no-brainer to spend our limited money," says Martin. "When we could all of a sudden do two things at once—get more space in the basement at the same time that we were getting a new washer and dryer and saving water—it all made a lot of sense."

The space they created also embodied this principle in terms of design; the new basement featured a tidy storage space under the stairs that helped for organization and a pullout bed so their basement TV room could double as a guest bedroom. They made sure that when they selected interior paint for the walls that it was low in volatile organic compounds (VOCs).

Add green features and increase the value

Room by room, item by item, Martin and Melissa fell in love with their increasingly beautiful and more efficient home. They never thought they'd leave, but life had other plans: Martin got a job in Milwaukee. After a year of long commutes, the couple decided it was time to move on.

The Scanlans hadn't been thinking about resale value as they made green improvements over the years. In fact, it took sitting down with their real estate agent, Sara Alvarado, to realize the marketing potential they had created while greening their home.

"Sara kept asking us more and more questions about what we had done to the home, and she pulled together marketing materials that highlighted the green features," Martin says. "We were grateful for that, because it definitely made a difference in being able to sell the house and maximize our investment."

The housing market in Madison had changed dramatically in the years since Martin and Melissa had bought their home. Buyers were choosier and houses were no longer being snatched up overnight. A house down the street had been on the market for over a year. But with their green pedigree as a selling point, the Scanlans beat the odds. In a few months, their home sold to a buyer who understood the value of green.

THE SYSTEMS ZONE: GREEN SPELLS QUIET AND COMFORTABLE

Green Your Home Adventurers:
Ron and Shelly Suzuki of Winnipeg, Manitoba

Their Home: A 1950s-era, one-and-a-half story cottage of 1,300 square feet

Their Green Improvements

- 2 inches of rigid Styrofoam insulation in the exterior walls

- Extending the rigid insulation on the ground 4 feet around the perimeter of the house to keep heat in the basement

- New insulation in the attic

- Triple-paned windows

- A brand-new, 95 percent-efficient furnace

- Dual-flush toilets and a high-efficiency washer and dryer that save 15,000 gallons of water a year

- A reframed metal roof made of recycled material

Their Story

Ron and Shelly Suzuki bought their home in 1991 and immediately went to work on improving it. Ron's father had been a custom home builder, so Ron had learned to swing a hammer in the summers of his youth. At the time of the first project, which included raising a steeply pitched roof to get more useful space out of the second floor, green wasn't on the Suzukis' radar.

"I drove an SUV, just like everyone else," Ron admits. But he began to develop a deep concern for his impact on the planet as a result of his passion for windsurfing on Lake Winnipeg. "I started reading about climate change and all the data and studies that have been done, and it's definitely an issue. I don't know where the line comes from, but 'If you're not part of the solution, you're part of the problem' is something that reverberates with me."

Efficiency is another word for comfort

Ron and Shelly know far too well how drafts and leaks interfere with comfort. The building envelope of their home left much to be desired. Before the Suzukis embarked upon their home's efficiency overhaul, the second-floor bedrooms would get so hot in summer that they would sleep in the basement to stay cool. In the winter, frost would develop on the baseboards and their puppy would cry because she was so cold. Their investment in insulation technologies changed everything.

The couple installed 2 inches of rigid Styrofoam insulation in the exterior walls, bringing the R-value rating up from R-8 to R-18. The R-value of insulation reflects the material's ability to resist the passage of heat and cold. The higher the number, the better. An added bonus was that the improvement was partially funded by a Manitoba Hydro Utility Services rebate. The Suzukis also extended the rigid insulation on the ground 4 feet around the perimeter of the house to keep heat in the basement, and insulated the attic with a Roxul product that keeps its insulation value even when wet!

Not only is their house now cooler in the summer and warmer in the winter, but tightening the building envelope and getting a new furnace have brought a number of spin-off benefits: The insulation does double-duty as soundproofing, their natural gas use has dropped 70 percent, and they no longer have to turn up the volume on the TV to drown out the hum of the furnace! Also, Ron estimates he is saving 5 tons of greenhouse gases a year. "Think about if everyone did that!" he says.

Work with experts who can help you prioritize

Ron estimates he spent two years and 1,000 hours on his home, working closely with skilled tradespeople, like masons and electricians, who could bring the skills he lacked. Because he enjoys remodeling, he suspects that he'll "never" be done improving his home, so it helps to have third-party experts assess which upgrades are most pressing and in what order they should be tackled.

"You need to do the things you'll get the most return on, and that will vary from region to region," Ron says. "In some places, water is very valuable. For us, electricity is very inexpensive, but natural gas is more expensive."

Invest in improvements that last a lifetime

Ron was scraping off old asphalt shingles to make way for the new metal roof when he had an epiphany: He was about to throw 3,000 pounds of asphalt into the landfill, as would thousands of other Winnipeggers that year.

"Every house in the city is doing this every twenty years," he says. "All of it is going in the landfill."

That realization made him feel extra good about his metal roof, which is made from recycled material, measured to fit his home perfectly, and will last for at least seventy-five years.

"This is the last roof I'll ever put on," says Ron. "My philosophy is: I'm going to do it right, so it's the last time I'll ever have to do it."

THE OUTSIDE ZONE: CREATING A HIGH-FUNCTIONING YARD

Green Your Home Adventurers:
Greg and Susan Corman of Tucson, Arizona

Their Home: A 1961 ranch house originally surrounded by Bermuda grass and a few Chinese junipers

Their Green Improvements

- Planting rescued mesquite trees

- Incorporating a stunning array of hardy native plants

- A new patio and walkways

- An extensive rainwater collection system

Their Story

Greg and Susan Corman had only lived in their house about six months when they hired a landscape designer to transform their neglected yard into a native paradise. The previous owners were "clearly not outdoors people," says Greg. They hadn't even figured out how to use the sliding glass doors to the patio! As you can imagine, the yard was very much a blank canvas.

Work with a landscape architect who understands your vision

Greg hired a designer who came well-recommended by friends, and the team got to work. However, their visions seemed more clashing than complementary: Greg and Susan wanted to enhance the midcentury modern vibe to the house, while the designer wanted to transform it into a different feel. In the end, the Cormans sent the designer on his way and never used much of what he recommended.

"It's really important to find a designer who understands your space and what you want out of it," says Greg, who subsequently became a landscape designer himself. "A designer isn't going to have all the ideas. Someone who lives in a house every day of the year will know more about how the house feels than I ever will. What a designer can do is come in with fresh eyes and help you see possibilities and potential you might not be seeing."

Find plants in creative places

Greg and Susan's front walkway is framed by fabulous native mesquites. These arching, mature trees didn't come from a nursery; they were rescued from a site that was about to be developed for housing. Because the trees are native to the area, they were helpful in creating a maintainable and sustainable landscape.

"If I had bought them retail, they would have been $3,000 apiece," says Greg. "Working with native plant groups, you can often find not only trees, but cacti and other native plants, cheap or free for the taking on predevelopment sites."

Take advantage of rainwater harvesting

The Corman home was appropriately designed for passive solar efficiency in Tucson's desert climate—huge overhangs and a central courtyard keep the residents cool and comfortable for most of the year. The large footprint of their home also means that a large portion of the lot is covered with impervious surfaces that can't absorb rainwater. By developing a rainwater harvesting system, Greg was able to capture that water off the roof and courtyard, rather than letting it run off into the driveway and be wasted. In essence, he doubled the natural rainfall on his yard by using a rainwater collection system.

"Very little water that hits this property leaves," says Greg. "The front yard is off irrigation. I haven't watered it in a couple years, except for new plantings. It's all taking care of itself and thriving."

Make your outdoor spaces multifunctional

When Greg and Susan moved into their home, the yard was little more than a green buffer around the house. Now, it's a multifunctional environment where every inch provides value for its owners. The courtyard and patio have enabled the Cormans to take their living areas outside, with open-air spaces that are perfect for appreciating the great outdoors. Sculptural plantings of native cacti and paloverde provide aesthetic interest. Citrus trees, vegetables, and herb gardens provide fresh food for their dining room table. The yard is wildlife-friendly, thanks to plants that attract hummingbirds and butterflies. There's even a rock pile for lizards to nest in. It's an environment that Greg and Susan can't keep themselves out of.

"We live in our backyard," says Greg.